W9-CPL-446

This Is a Tree

A sycamore tree in winter

65-5250

This Is a Tree

ROSS E. HUTCHINS

Photographs by the author

DODD, MEAD & COMPANY

NEW YORK

RODMAN PUBLIC LIBRARY

All photographs are by the author except the following: pages 100, 104, 105 courtesy of Save-the-Redwoods League, San Francisco, California; page 109, courtesy of Rutgers University, New Brunswick, New Jersey.

Copyright © 1964 by Ross E. Hutchins
All rights reserved. No part of this book may be reproduced
in any form without permission in writing from the publisher.
Library of Congress Catalog Card Number: 64-11517
Printed in the United States of America

TO
DR. C. M. GOETHE
who, during his long life,
has contributed so much to the
preservation of America's wild places

Introduction

Imagine, if you can, a world without trees. Most of us take trees for granted, never thinking what amazing things they really are or the important part they have played in shaping man's history.

The primitive man who first fitted a spearhead to a wooden shaft and used it to kill a wild beast had taken the initial step that committed his race to an important place in history. He had invented the spear, a weapon which extended his reach beyond the length of his own arms. His next step up the ladder also involved wood. He learned the secret of fire and how to control it for useful purposes. To ancient man this was even more important than the splitting of the atom was to the modern world.

As time passed, man learned other uses for trees and their products. From them he could build shelters against the cold of winter and dugout canoes for crossing streams and lakes. In time he learned how to construct great wooden ships that could be driven by winds across the world's largest seas. This expanded his domain and soon he found other lands to conquer. Later, of course, he built wooden airplanes and his conquest of the air began.

Too, there came a time in man's history when he began to record his thoughts and ideas for others to read. At first he inscribed his words on clay tablets, but, finding these too cumbersome, he turned to paper made from plant and wood fibers. Thus, with the help of trees, man records and preserves his knowledge.

The admiration of trees for their grace and beauty is almost universal. Is it any wonder, then, that our remote ancestors actually worshiped trees and believed they had souls?

Of all the world's plants, trees are perhaps the most remarkable. The life of a tree stretches across the lives of many men. Some trees reach great age and in their time have seen civilizations rise and fall and great nations come into flower and pass away. All this has occurred during the life of a single tree, which year by year grew larger and recorded the passage of time in its growth rings.

Trees are masterpieces of engineering and chemistry, from the hidden roots that anchor them to the earth to the countless leaves far above in the sun where the miracle of photosynthesis or food manufacture takes place.

This, then, is the story of trees recorded on paper, a product of the forest.

— R. E. H.

Contents

Introduction   7

1. What Is a Tree?   11

2. The Life Within   23

3. The Leaf and the Needle   41

4. Trees and Their Flowers   59

5. From Little Seeds   73

6. Tree Rings — Keys to the Past   87

7. The Big and the Famous   101

8. Of Woods and Men   115

9. The Things They Make   129

10. The World of the Tree   143

Index   156

A magnolia tree, one of an ancient race of trees that began nearly a hundred million years ago. Its ancestors were among the first flowering trees.

CHAPTER 1

What Is a Tree?

Trees are different things to different people. To the Druids of ancient England, trees, especially oaks, were sacred beings to be worshiped as deities. In almost all European countries trees were once believed to be endowed with souls and, in Germany, anyone who mutilated a tree was frequently punished by death. One of the most sacred objects in ancient Rome was a cornel tree (probably a dogwood) which was carefully watched for any sign of ill health. In many countries of the ancient world human sacrifices were often made to tree gods, with appropriate pagan ceremonies. Trees were believed to be inhabited by spirits, both good and bad. Similar beliefs were held by American Indians, who frequently refused to cut down trees lest misfortune befall the tribe. In some countries it was formerly the custom to "ask" a tree's permission, or offer it gifts, before it was cut down. On the other hand, Japanese farmers often ask a fruit tree whether or not it is going to bear fruit, at the same time threatening it with an ax. Perhaps this is a practical approach that gets results!

It was once a common belief, in many lands, that trees were possessed of great knowledge. It was reasoned that their deep roots penetrated down into the underworld, the abode of departed spirits. From these spirits, it was believed, the tree absorbed the wisdom of the ages and could foresee the future.

The tree gods were consulted about events that were to come. The Hindus hold the pipal, or sacred fig tree, in great respect. It is a relative of the banyan and grows to great size and lives to great age. It is believed that if a person lies while holding a pipal leaf in the hand, that person will be crushed to death. Sacred pipal trees are never destroyed. There is a legend that Buddha sat under a bo tree—a fig—for seven days in contemplation before going forth to preach Buddhism. As a result, bo trees are planted near Buddhist temples. Many trees down the centuries have been considered as holy or endowed with spiritual significance. The holly was once called "holy wood."

Trees have a long and proud history. At one time great forests of gigantic tree ferns and horsetails covered almost the entire world. This was a hundred million years before the age of the giant reptiles or dinosaurs. But the climates of the world changed, and the ancient forms of life slowly passed away. The

The strangler fig gradually encircles and strangles the tree upon which it begins growth. Here it is a sabal palm that is doomed.

Many millions of years ago this tree grew beside a lake in the Mississippi Valley. It fell into the water and eventually became petrified. Notice the growth rings in the end.

primitive pines came into being and spread across the world. Later they were joined by the broad-leaf trees that eventually became the ancestors of the oaks, hickories, elms, and all the other trees of the modern world that add so much to our lives.

Fig trees once grew in Greenland, and places now buried under ice were once graced by growths of magnolias and other trees of warm climates. Some of these ancient trees were blown down in wind storms and sank to the bottoms of prehistoric lakes where they slowly turned to stone. These petrified trees can be seen in many places where the ancient lake beds have been eroded away. Such fossil trees give us hints of the past when climates were warmer and the world's forests were in their glory.

We no longer believe that trees are inhabited by spirits or that their cutting brings curses upon us, yet trees are majestic things admired by all of us. It is little wonder that the peoples of the ancient world regarded them with such veneration. Even today, a few of the old superstitions still remain. We still decorate trees at Christmas, a custom that comes down to us from ancient pagan ceremonies. The happy role of the Christmas tree

13

during the Yule season actually originated in Germany but was unheard of in America prior to the Revolutionary War. Maypole dances are still held in some countries, and these, too, have a pagan origin. Perhaps the most interesting tree superstition is that of using their branches to locate water sources. In several countries—our own included—many people still believe that underground springs may be located by walking about with a branch, or "divining rod," held in the hands. When a spot is reached over hidden water, a pull is supposed to be felt on the branch. Such methods of locating water are called *dowsing,* and a variety of tree branches and twigs are used. The Chinese use peach branches, but the ancient Druids placed more faith in apple. The witch hazel was once especially favored, which explains its name, since this method of locating water is also called "witching." It is not a thing of the past. There is actually an organization called The American Society of Dowsers with 25,000 members. It holds national meetings.

How often have we "knocked on wood" to ward off some accident? This, too, comes from an ancient superstition. Long ago it was believed that trees were the homes of gods and, if a person had a favor to ask, he touched the bark. If the favor was granted, he knocked on the tree as a token of thanks. Even the children's game of "tree tag" is based on an old superstition that touching a tree made one safe from harm.

In the Great Smoky Mountains there is a place where a mountain stream tumbles down through a virgin stand of forest giants. When walking through this forest one has the feeling of being in a great cathedral where, from far overhead, the songs of birds filter down like the sound of a distant choir. This is a bit of the great American forest that remains the same as it was when the Pilgrims landed, the same as it had existed for thousands of years before the settlers' axes began their destruction. Such forests are places where men can retreat to solitude and peace.

All of us admire trees for their beauty and symmetry of form.

14

Because of their size, trees are often used by vines to creep up to the sunlight. This is a wild grape vine.

The shapes of trees are infinite, varying from the cigar-shaped Lombardy poplars of northern climates to spreading live oaks draped with Spanish moss in the warm lands bordering the Gulf of Mexico. The weeping willow and weeping birch have especially characteristic manners of growth. Some people admire the flowering trees beyond all others, from magnolias with their huge white blossoms to the royal poincianas of tropical countries. I once saw what I thought was a native hut on fire in a tropical forest, but when I approached more closely I found it

15

In winter when a tree's limbs are bare, the characteristic framework shows up in all its detail. This is an elm. (See photograph opposite.)

to be a royal poinciana covered with brilliant flame-colored blooms. Even the ground beneath the great tree was carpeted with the scarlet petals. This is usually considered to be the world's most beautiful flowering tree.

The trees of summer have their quiet beauty, but with the coming of autumn Nature tints the hills of northern climates with gold and scarlet. To many tree lovers this is a favorite time of the year, but even in winter, when their limbs stand etched against the sky, trees are attractive things. Deep woods in winter are far different from the same places in summer. It is then that the true symmetry of trees becomes evident. The white trunks and limbs of the sycamores and birches stand out against the darker forest trees. If we are familiar enough with trees we can recognize the various kinds by their characteristic manners of growth, even when their foliage is gone.

16

The same elm tree in summer when it is draped with foliage. Those familiar with trees can recognize various kinds with or without leaves.

Each year, Americans in increasing thousands visit our National Parks and other forested areas to enjoy wild nature. Where permitted, some people come to hunt the game that still abounds, but others are content merely to watch and study nature in its natural surroundings. To each, whatever his interest, such forests afford a degree of pleasure and satisfaction. To the lumberman, on the other hand, a forest exists in terms of lumber, board feet and dollars, but this is his contribution to our economic life. Without this great natural resource our lives would be far different.

But what is so wonderful about trees? Are they not just big plants? Why have men down the centuries looked at trees and seen them as special beings endowed with souls? These questions are a little hard to answer. It is true that trees are actually overgrown plants belonging to many families. In a few plant

17

families, such as the pine, oak, and hickory families, all the members are trees. In other families, trees are the exception, most members being small and not at all treelike. Mesquite, mimosa, locust, redbud and acacia all belong to the pea family. As a matter of fact, many of the most majestic trees of tropical forests, such as ipil, belong to this group. In South America there is a tree-size member of the sunflower family that is actually cut for its lumber. Most of us know lobelias as small, attractive flowering plants, but in East Africa, there are strange, treelike lobelias that grow 30 feet tall. Perhaps the most unusual tree of all is the dragon tree, found in several places, including the Canary Islands. Very large, sometimes reaching a height of 70 feet and a diameter of 40 feet, they belong to the lily family!

Thus, we have trees and treelike plants, but where is the dividing line? If we cut down a tree fern or a palm and study the structure of its stem or trunk we find that it differs greatly from that of a pine or an oak. The trunks of the latter trees are composed of yearly growth rings while the tree ferns and palms do not have these yearly growth rings. Still, we cannot say that only large plants having yearly growth rings are true trees. A dictionary defines a tree as a woody perennial plant having a single main axis or stem, commonly exceeding ten feet in height, and bearing a definite crown of leaves and branches. That is, perhaps, as good a definition as any, but what about Arctic birches that grow only ten inches tall? Or stunted pines on high, wind-swept ridges of the Rockies which may struggle along for a hundred years and still only reach a height of a few feet? Size does not determine which is a tree and which is not.

In general, a tree is a perennial plant that lives for many years, sometimes for many centuries. It has permanent aerial parts—trunks and branches. Only its leaves, and sometimes its twigs, are periodically worn out, shed, and replaced. In northern climates this occurs each season, but in tropical lands the loss and replacement is not so abrupt or noticeable. Annual plants,

The bald cypress often grows in water but sends up "knees" or pneumato-phores from the roots to obtain air. These trees were photographed at low water when the "knees" were exposed.

The royal palm is considered by many to be the most stately of trees. It grows to 125 feet and bears edible fruit.

such as flowers, usually grow to a certain height then flower and die, but a tree continues to grow year after year as long as it lives, whether this be twenty or five thousand years. A tree, like any other plant, is a living, breathing thing even though it remains anchored to one spot throughout its life. Within its great body, water and minerals flow upward from the hidden roots and out through the countless branches and twigs to the leaves where starches and sugars are manufactured and sent downward through other tubes to nourish the tree's many parts. On a summer day a tree may look very quiet with only its leaves trembling in the breeze, yet beneath its bark wonderful things are taking place. It is a complex chemical manufacturing plant where raw materials are being slowly transformed into the many products needed by the growing tree. It is continually performing miracles that no laboratory built by the hand of man can duplicate. Ancient pagan tribes that once danced around their sacred trees regarded them with awe, but had they known what we know today, they would have held these trees in even greater esteem. Our modern knowledge of the wonders of trees' living and growing processes should certainly make us appreciate them even more.

The mangrove grows with its "feet" in salt water. Its prop roots continually reach out and form new attachments to the bottom for support.

This tupelo gum tree has an extra large base and root system to help it resist the pressure of winds.

At the entrance to a public park in Portugal, there is a sign that reads:

Ye who would pass by and raise your hand against me, harken ere you harm me. I am the heat of your hearth on the cold winter nights; the friendly shade screening you from the summer sun; and my fruits are refreshing draughts quenching your thirst as you journey on. I am the beam that holds your house, the board of your table, the bed on which you lie, and the timber that builds your boat. I am the handle of your hoe, the door of your homestead, the wood of your cradle, and the shell of your coffin. I am the gift of God and friend of man.

21

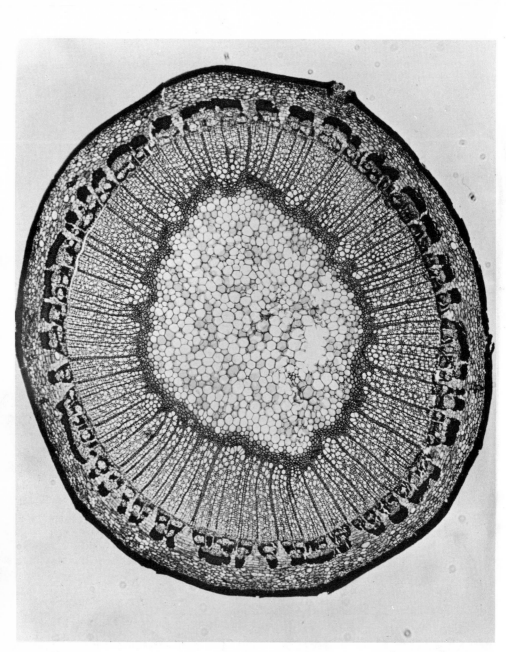

This is a microscopic view of the cross-section of a one-year-old tulip poplar. At the center is the pith, surrounded by the annual growth ring of summerwood or xylem. This is followed by the circular cambium layer, and just beyond are many phloem areas. The bark forms a protective layer on the outside.

CHAPTER 2

The Life Within

*I*f you cut a notch in a living tree, you will see little of interest; there appears to be nothing but white wood. Yet when one studies the structure of a living tree and finds out about the complexity of its parts and how they work, one quickly realizes that it is a very remarkable thing indeed. We can begin by studying the sawed end of a piece of fire wood, or a stump. The most obvious things are the growth rings which surround the heart in concentric circles, one after another, until the bark is reached. One of these rings is usually produced each year, and thus we can easily determine the age of the tree. If we study the cut end of the log or stump more closely with a hand lens, we can see additional details, but if we look at the wood through a microscope we can see even more remarkable things. Biologists cut very thin slices—thinner than this page—across the stems of trees and, after staining and cementing them to glass slides, are able to study them under microscopes. Photographs can also be taken of these cross-sections. If you will study the photograph of the microscopic view of a cross-section of a one-year-old tulip poplar stem, you will see that it reveals the minute details of a typical tree stem or trunk. The basic structure of most trees is about the same, whether they be oak, gum, pine or poplar.

At the center of a typical tree trunk is an area of heartwood. The size of this varies with the species, and it is actually dead

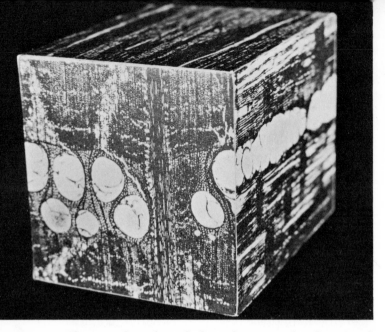

This greatly enlarged three-dimensional cube of oak wood shows its structure. Note the large ducts that carry water and dissolved minerals up the trunk. Compare this with the yellow pine on the next page.

wood, serving the tree only in giving it support. Sometimes old trees may be almost completely hollow, the heartwood having decayed. This does not appear to injure the tree, however, except to render it more easily damaged by winds. In the case of a giant Sequoia, the heartwood has been dead for thousands of years, yet this dead wood is solid and unaffected by decay, and time has left it untouched. In most kinds of trees only the outer portion of the wood is alive, often only the outer two or three annual rings. In a walnut tree two feet in diameter, there is a layer of living wood only two inches thick.

The layers of wood surrounding the heartwood are called *sapwood,* made up of recently produced annual rings of growth, and it is through the hollow or porous cells that make up these layers that water and dissolved minerals flow upward from the roots to the branches and leaves. This woody zone surrounding the heart is called *xylem,* a word derived from the Greek word *xylon,* meaning "wood." Sapwood is usually lighter in color than heartwood, but in some trees, such as cottonwood, birch and pine, the difference is not very obvious. In the case of cedar, willow, walnut and oak, on the other hand, there is a distinct difference in coloration, the heartwood being darker. Heartwood is usually more durable than sapwood and, thus, is much more desirable to the lumberman.

Each year a new, annual ring of xylem cells is produced. The inner part of the annual ring is produced in spring, while growth is rapid, and is made up of thin-walled cells with large pores; the outer portion is produced in summer and its cells have thicker walls and there are smaller pores.

Before living xylem cells die and become non-living wood, their cell walls are strengthened by the addition of fibers and hard *lignin*. This prevents them from collapsing when water is pumped or pulled upward through them. This also adds strength to the wood. It is an interesting fact that the xylem cells, through which water and minerals flow upward through the trunk, fulfill their destiny only after they are dead. As living cells they perform no useful work.

A three-dimensional cube of yellow pine. The surface at left shows two springwood zones (thin-walled cells) and two summerwood zones (thick-walled cells). At right, vascular rays which transport fluids crosswise.

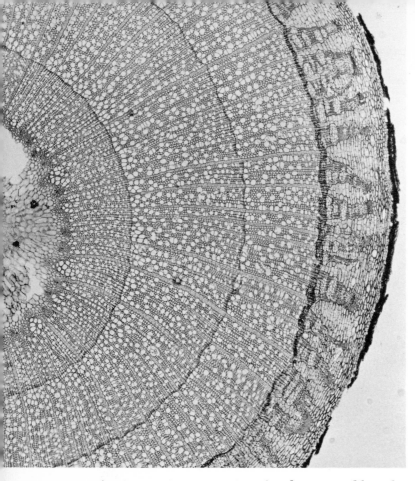

A microscopic cross-section of a three-year-old poplar stem. The heart is at left. Note the three zones of porous summerwood and radiating vascular rays. The phloem and bark are at right. Compare this with the cross-section of the one-year-old poplar stem.

A typical tree trunk contains countless billions of cells of various kinds. It has been estimated that if a man were to begin counting the cells in a single layer on a large tree stump at the rate of 200 a minute, nearly 2,000 years would be required to count them all!

When autumn arrives, tree growth suddenly comes to a stop in northern climates and a tree's life processes become dormant. With the coming of spring the tree begins growing again and starts the production of another growth ring. How this alternation between springwood and summerwood appears under a

26

microscope can be seen by referring to the photograph of the three-year-old poplar stem. The microscopic view shows a number of "rays" extending outward through the woody xylem. These are bundles of xylem cells called "vascular rays" which extend across the other xylem cells, and their work consists of transporting fluids and dissolved foods crosswise through the trunk of the tree. New vascular rays are added as the tree grows larger; thus, the distance between them remains more or less constant. The presence of these rays, along with the annual rings of growth, gives woods of various kinds their characteristic appearances when they have been sawed into lumber.

An examination of various tree woods under a hand lens or microscope will reveal several differences. In the case of a hard wood such as oak, there are relatively large ducts through which water passes up through the trunk. The xylem ducts have open ends so that water can pass freely up through the wood. On the other hand, a microscopic examination of pine—a soft wood—reveals that there are no real ducts. The ends of the cells overlap and water passing upward from one cell to the next passes through pits from cell to cell.

Pine wood cut vertically to show lengthwise structure. The hollow cells conduct water up the stem. The groups of vascular ray cells carry fluids crosswise through the stem.

The xylem or wood of a typical tree is composed mostly of cellulose, the chief constituent of cotton. The tree produces this material out of the sugars which are manufactured by the busy leaves with the aid of sunlight. Interestingly, cellulose can be broken down again into sugars and used by us as animal food and in the production of wood alcohol. The rest of the xylem is composed of hard lignin, and of fats, resins, tannins and other things. The cellulose, however, is the most important constituent of wood and is the chief material used in the manufacture of paper, cardboard, and all the allied products.

The amount of wood in a tree is, of course, of tremendous importance to a forester. It is calculated in terms of board feet, a board foot being a piece of wood one foot square and one inch thick. Foresters estimate the number of board feet in a tree by means of special scales or measuring devices. A tree measuring 24 inches in diameter will yield about 250 board feet for each usable 16-foot log which can be cut from it. The total amount of wood in a large tree is often quite amazing. In some giant Sequoias there may be as much as *50,000* cubic feet in a single tree. This amount of wood would make a solid block 36 feet on each side, a block that would be about three stories high and contain enough wood, if sawed into lumber, to build a whole residential subdivision consisting of thirty-five houses. In our modern world it is difficult to imagine the vast amounts of wood products used each year. One example may be enlightening. The wood pulp needed to make the paper for a single Sunday edition of *The New York Times* amounts to 800 cords. (A cord is a stack of 4-foot logs, four feet high and eight feet long.) The equivalent of 80 acres of woodland must be cut each day to supply that amount of pulp wood. In order to supply this great newspaper continuously, a stand of 416,000 acres of forest must be maintained.

As the years pass and a tree grows, it becomes larger and larger in circumference, but it is only at the tip or tips of its main trunk that height increase occurs. It grows upward only at the top. If you carve your initials on a tree and visit it many years later you will find that, even though the tree is much larger around and much taller, your initials are at the same height as when you carved them. This proves that the tree does not grow upward from the roots.

Returning to our exploration of the tree trunk, we find, just beyond the xylem or wood, a thin zone of cells. This is the *cambium* and it is very important to the living tree. As a matter of fact, this layer of cells is like a living blanket that completely surrounds the wood and extends from the growing tip of the tree down to the roots. In most instances it is only three or four cells thick. These cells are continually multiplying and separating away; those separating toward the inside become new additions to the xylem, while those produced on the outside of the cambium layer develop into the "inner bark" which we see as a slick, white layer in the case of a pine tree. This so-called inner bark, however, has a very important function, and the tree could not live without it. It is made up of numerous cells and is called *phloem* tissue. Within this layer are sieve tubes, phloem fibers and other cells. Many primitive tribes take advantage of the hard phloem fibers of certain tropical trees in the making of bark "cloth." The inner bark of the cloth-bark tree of Africa and of the lace-bark tree of tropical America is stripped off and pounded into a soft but fairly durable fabric used for making wearing apparel. Other plants besides trees also possess these phloem fibers. Linen cloth is derived from the phloem fibers of flax, and jute and hemp have phloem fibers of economic value.

The sieve tubes of the inner bark, or phloem tissue, consist of elongate cells with perforated ends. Foods manufactured by the leaves flow downward through these sieve tubes to nourish the various tree parts, including the roots. You will recall that water and dissolved minerals pass upward from the roots through the inner wood or xylem. Thus, we see that the "circulatory" system of a tree follows two paths, one path flowing upward through the dead xylem to the leaves, and the other flowing downward through the living phloem or inner bark. We should remember, however, that a tree—or any other plant—does not have a circulatory system in the sense that we do. Our blood vessels carry our blood around through our bodies in a closed system. In trees there are two separate systems, one to carry materials up from the roots and another to transport manufactured products downward. We often take advantage of this downward flow of manufactured products in the case of pines. These trees are "turpentined" by cutting through the phloem and catching the turpentine and rosin which flow downward and ooze out.

Sometimes unwanted trees that are to be removed are "ringed"; that is, an ax is used to cut deep grooves around the trees through the bark, phloem and cambium layers to the wood. Such trees may continue to live for some time and may even leaf out and bloom for a year or two. This is possible because the xylem or woody tissue continues to carry water and minerals upward from the roots. But a ringed tree will eventually die because the vital cambium has been destroyed and no new growth can occur. Also, the cutting of the phloem stops the

This view of an Osage orange or bois d'arc trunk shows the annual growth rings, the dark golden heartwood, the white sapwood and the bark. Compare it with the cross-section of pine on the next page.

The growth rings in this pine tree are clearly seen, but there is no differ-ence in the color of the sapwood and heartwood as in the Osage orange. Note that some of the growth rings are wider than others. This was caused by different amounts of rainfall during years when the rings were formed.

passage of manufactured foods downward to nourish the roots and other parts of the tree.

The entire outside of the tree's trunk is surrounded by the bark. This has a protective function and varies in thickness from a fraction of an inch to two feet in the case of large Douglas firs or Sequoias. As a tree increases in size the bark stretches, and cracks appear on the outer surface. This accounts for the fissur-ing of pine and other tree barks. Outer bark cells are corklike and dead; their walls contain a fatty substance called *suberin* which prevents the passage of water and gases through the bark, and helps the tree conserve water. Bark cells are light and filled with air, which makes them an excellent insulating layer against both heat and cold. In fact, trees having very thick bark are so well protected that they can withstand the heat of very severe forest fires. There is a large tree in Central America closely re-lated to balsa, the *Cavanillesia platanifolia*, that has very thick and tough bark. Since the wood is very weak, it is the bark that actually supports the tree.

31

As a pine increases in size, fissures appear in the bark. Pine bark is thick and filled with air cells, a good insulator against the heat of forest fires.

Tree bark, like our own skin, is chiefly a protective covering and, as such, often contains substances which repel insects and diseases. The bark of some trees contains large amounts of bitter tannin, while other kinds have acids, gums or waxes. The bark of many trees is set with spines which protect them from climbing animals. Examples are prickly ash, honey locust and devil's club. The bark of prickly ash also contains a substance which causes tingling sensations in the mouth of any creature that gnaws into it. But tree bark is useful to us. That of the South American cinchona tree contains quinine. Birch bark was once peeled off and used in the making of canoes by northern Indians. Cork stoppers are cut from the thick bark of the cork oak, grown chiefly in Spain.

As a tree grows taller its growing tip pushes upward, but at the same time the vital cambium layer is producing new layers of cells on its inner and outer surfaces. The tree becomes larger and larger in diameter, and its roots are, of course, also growing. By contrast, an animal gradually grows larger in all its parts as compared to a tree which grows only by the addition of new outer growth rings and increases in height and root length.

Foresters have sensitive instruments called *dendrometers* which they attach to tree trunks to measure their growth rates. By means of these instruments some quite interesting facts have been discovered. Trees rarely grow continuously during the en-

Many trees can be recognized by their bark. Note the shingled appearance of this bark of white oak.

The trunk of the devil's club tree is protected by circles of sharp spines.

The bark of the hackberry tree is readily recognized. As the tree grows older its bark develops characteristic tubercles of interesting shapes.

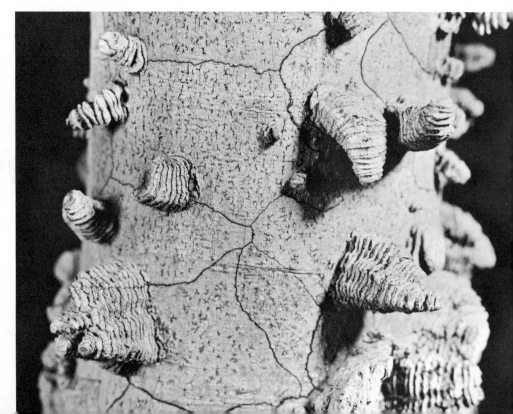

tire summer. The period of most rapid growth occurs in early spring, but as the season progresses, it slows down and finally stops. And the periods of trunk growth and height increase may not be exactly the same. In other words, these two types of growth start and end at different times. As a general rule, increase in height generally slows down earlier in the summer than diameter growth. Too, there are differences in growth rates between night and day. Shoots often grow almost twice as fast during the night as during the day. Growth records were kept of some loblolly pines in North Carolina, and it was found that during the day they grew about an inch-and-a-half in length, while at night the growth rate sped up and they grew more than three inches.

Many things, of course, affect tree growth. Drought slows up growth, as does defoliation by insects or diseases. Heavy rains after dry periods often cause sudden spurts of growth. As we will see later, such abrupt changes in growth rates are faithfully recorded in the growth rings.

It is a characteristic of many trees that most of their growth occurs during a very short period. In the case of red oak, beech, white ash and jack pine, most of the summer's growth occurs during the first month of spring. Other trees—aspen, birch, yellow poplar—seem slower in getting started, most of the year's growth occurring in mid-summer. The seasonal growth rates of some trees are difficult to explain. It was found that several kinds of oaks in the Ozark Mountains made 90 per cent of their growth during a three-week period in spring.

As one might expect, trees with short lives grow the fastest. The redwoods, which may live for several thousand years, grow quite slowly, whereas a cottonwood may shoot up rapidly but live for only a few years. One kind of mimosa tree reaches a height of nearly 90 feet in only seven years.

Most trees have definite forms of growth, and we can often identify a tree in winter by its silhouette. Throughout their lives trees are in a continual struggle for places in the sun, sunlight being necessary for growth. They reach both upward and outward to hold as many leaves as possible to the sun and air, so in a sense, all trees are sun worshipers. On a summer day a forest appears quiet, but if we could see a forest in a greatly speeded-up movie we would be amazed. We would see some trees thrusting upward above the rest while others, because of slower growth, were overshadowed. Some of these slow-growers would continue to survive, but others would gradually die in the forest gloom. It is a general rule that shade tolerant trees grow more slowly than those that need much light, which is perhaps to be expected.

This brings us to the interesting subject of *apical dominance*. In plain language, this means that the apical, or growing tip, of a tree often governs the growth of its lower branches. The growing tip produces certain chemical regulators or *auxins* that flow downward and prevent, or slow down, the growth of lower branches. In the case of pine, for example, if the central tip is cut off or injured in any way so that there are no growth-slowing auxins flowing downward through the trunk, the side branches begin growing. One of these will eventually replace the old growing tip that was lost or injured. Within a couple of years the new tip cannot be distinguished from the original. In the case of a many-branched tree like the elm, the terminal buds are shed. This results in the growth of many branches from lateral buds. Eventually, the original, central stem disappears and we have a fan-shaped tree. Thus does Nature control the growth and shape of trees through the use of chemical regulators.

Botanists divide trees into two types according to their styles of growth. The pines and spruces, which thrust upward from a central growing tip, are called "excurrent." Most other trees, such as elms and oaks, spread their branches out in a fan-shaped pattern with no central trunk reaching to the top of the tree.

36

A tree grows in height only at its tip. This is a cutaway view of the growing tip of a small pine tree. A chemical regulator is secreted here which flows downward, slowing the growth of lower branches.

These are called "deliquescent." The word means "to fade away" and that is what happens to the central stem. Such trees change their growth styles as they mature. At first they have "excurrent" growth like a pine, but later the lateral branches begin growing faster so that the central stem disappears.

We can often see the record of the forest struggle for light in a pine stump. The inner, or oldest, growth rings are wide, indicating rapid growth. During this period of their lives the trees were all small and received sufficient light and moisture. But as

37

the trees grew larger the forest became more and more crowded and growth slowed down. This change is recorded in the growth rings; they suddenly became narrower. Among trees, as among men, crowded living conditions restrict chances for full development, whether it be of growth or intellect.

Many of the growth processes in nature are involved with spirals. This is true of all plants as well as with many animals such as snails. Many parts of a tree are arranged in spirals including its twigs, leaves, buds, and the scales enclosing the seeds in the case of pines. Study the arrangement of the scales that make up a pine cone. You will notice that they form a tight spiral. Observe, also, the arrangement of the bases of pine needle bundles on the stem. They, too, are in spirals. Even tree limbs form a spiral up the trunk. This may not be obvious in an older tree because some branches are always broken off or shed during growth. But if a young tree is carefully studied it will be found that in most cases its branches are placed in a spiral arrangement up the trunk. Interestingly, too, each kind of tree has its own characteristic spiral. Some trees, such as the beech, have what is called a $\frac{1}{3}$ spiral. This means that if a string is wound around the tree passing over the bases of successive twigs up the stem, it will pass once around the tree and over the bases of three twigs before a twig is reached directly above the twig where the count began. Other trees, such as oaks and poplars, have $\frac{2}{5}$ spirals. In this case the string would go around the tree twice and pass over the bases of five twigs before reaching one directly above the one where count began. These are probably the two most common spiral types. The spirals, by the way, turn to either the right or left.

If possible spiral types found in various plants and trees are listed, they would be as follows: $\frac{1}{2}$, $\frac{1}{3}$, $\frac{2}{5}$, $\frac{3}{8}$, $\frac{5}{13}$, $\frac{8}{21}$, $\frac{13}{34}$, and so on. This is called a *Fibonacci* series. The higher the numbers, the tighter the spirals. The spiral arrangements of plant parts often go to great extremes, as in the case of the tight spirals of

Tree limbs grow in spirals around the trunk just as do the leaves of small, herbaceous plants. In old trees this is not very noticeable since many limbs are lost during growth.

pine cone scales or in the arrangement of daisy and sunflower heads. It was found that one large sunflower head had a $^{144}/_{377}$ spiral! Now if you will go back and examine the spiral sequence listed previously, you will notice something very interesting. If the numerators, or top numbers, of any two consecutive spiral types are added together, they will equal the numerator of the next spiral type. The same is true of the denominators, or lower numbers. Just why this is so is probably not understood, but the answer lies hidden somewhere in the basic genetics of plant growth.

Trees can usually be identified by their leaves. These leaves of sassafras are of three forms.

Botanists classify these red buckeye leaves as palmate.

CHAPTER 3

The Leaf and the Needle

$\mathcal{L}$ eaves are among the most common things in the world, and a casual examination of an individual specimen reveals little of interest. Yet, if we study a leaf, especially under a microscope, all its wonders are revealed. All its wonders, that is, except how it works. That is something scientists do not yet fully understand. They know all about how it is built and how water and minerals flow into it through minute ducts and how the starches and sugars it manufactures flow downward again to nourish the tree. They know that the green substance called *chlorophyll* traps the energy of the sun and uses this energy to make starch out of water and carbon dioxide gas. This process has been named *photosynthesis*, but merely giving it a convenient name does not explain how it works. So leaves are still mysterious things, even to scientists.

Tree leaves come in endless assorted sizes and shapes. They vary in form from the needle-like leaves of the pines to the huge leaves of the big-leaf magnolias and the 20-foot leaves of the palms. They are thick, thin, wide, narrow, smooth-margined and serrate-margined. In some cases the leaves are divided into smaller leaflets as in the locusts, buckeye and ash. These are called *compound* leaves as contrasted with *simple* leaves, such as those of willows. Botanists classify leaves according to their shapes and margins as follows:

Linear: needle-like. Example, pine.

Lanceolate: shaped like a lance-head, much longer than broad. Examples, hackberry and willow.

Ovate: egg-shaped. Examples, water tupelo, blackjack oak and dogwood.

Cordate: heart-shaped. Examples, cottonwood, redbud, catalpa and sycamore.

Stellate: star-shaped. Example, sweetgum.

Oblong: longer than broad. Examples, beech and birch.

Lobed: leaves divided into lobes. Examples, most oaks.

Palmate: divided into leaflets like the fingers of the hand. Example, buckeye.

Attenuate: tapering to a point. Examples, hackberry, elm and willow.

Crenate: margins with rounded teeth. Example, chestnut oak.

Serrate: margins with fine, sharp teeth pointing forward. Examples, chestnut, birch and elm.

Dentate: margins with large, sharp teeth pointing forward. Examples, gray birch and maple.

Spinose: margins of leaf with spines. Example, black or red oaks.

In most cases more than one of the above terms is used to describe a particular leaf. A chestnut leaf may be described as being narrowly oblong and dentate. A basswood leaf is heart-shaped with toothed margins, so a botanist would describe it as being cordate-dentate. In general, Nature has designed leaves so that large surface areas will be exposed to the sun. The total leaf surface exposed for light absorption is often quite amazing. A beech tree 15 inches in diameter was found to have 119,000 leaves with a total surface, both sides, of about 3,000 square feet. This is equal to a solid surface 55 feet square. Spruces and firs 15 inches in diameter may have from 10 to 20 million needles, while a 25-inch tree has about 40 million needles. A silver fir was also found to have 40 million needles, but the total exposed leaf or needle surface amounted to about 20,000 square feet, an area equal to that of ten tennis courts. But it is estimated that a 200-foot Douglas fir has about 30,000 square feet of leaf surface, the equivalent of nearly three acres! It might seem that the leaves of broad-leaf trees such as elms would have more

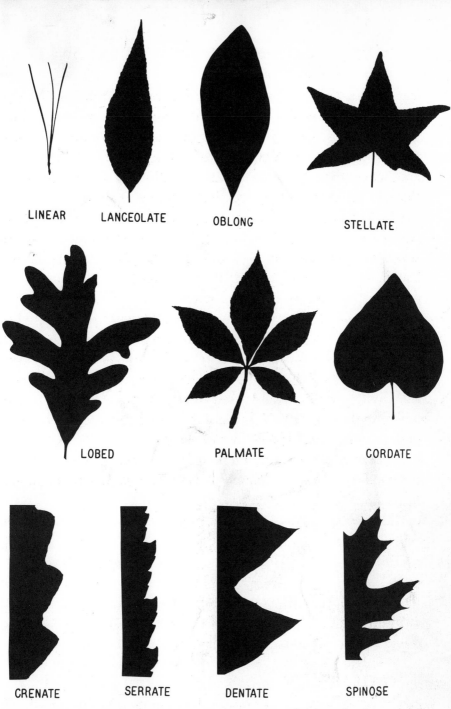

LINEAR LANCEOLATE OBLONG STELLATE

LOBED PALMATE CORDATE

CRENATE SERRATE DENTATE SPINOSE

The two top rows show a number of common leaf shapes. The shapes and examples of each are as follows: Linear, pine; lanceolate, elm; oblong, sassafras; stellate, sweet gum; lobed, white oak; palmate, buckeye; cordate, redbud. The bottom row shows types of leaf margins.

leaf surface exposed than pines or firs, but the truth is that the finely divided needles of these latter trees have more leaf surface and, thus, more chlorophyll for the manufacture of food.

Leaf size, even on the same tree, varies considerably. In general, leaves exposed to the full rays of the sun are smaller than those in the shade. Many trees also arrange their leaves in such a manner as to take advantage of all the sunlight possible. Elm and maple leaves vary in size on the same twig, but the small leaves are placed so as to fill the gaps left between the larger leaves. It is from the sun that leaves receive their supply of power or energy, yet it is a reflection on the efficiency of leaves that they actually use only a small percentage of the total light-energy that falls upon them. In some experiments it was found that, when the total light-energy of the sun falling on leaves amounted to 60,000 calories per square foot of leaf surface, only 320 calories were actually used in starch manufacture. On the other hand, about 10,000 calories of this light-energy were used to evaporate water. The rest was wasted.

Trees must have sunlight to live, but the heat of the sun often causes them to lose too much moisture for proper functioning.

The needles of pines are actually leaves. They are arranged in spirals on the twigs.

Leaves are usually arranged so that they do not overlap and cut off sunlight from the ones below. These devil's club tree leaves form a mosaic.

They must protect themselves, especially in dry regions. Leaves have many breathing pores or *stomates*, through which they breathe in air and pass out water and gases. These occur in large numbers on both surfaces, but there are more on the lower surface, probably because they are less apt to be clogged with dust in that location. There is a kidney-shaped cell on either side of each stomate. These *guard cells* expand and contract, opening and closing the gap between them. This controls the loss of water by the leaves. A Norway maple leaf has about 400 stomates per each square millimeter (a millimeter is about ⅟₃₂ of an inch). A black walnut leaf has somewhat more than this. An oak leaf may have as many as 1,400 per square millimeter.

As one might expect, desert plants have few stomates; they have to conserve what water is available. The ocotillo of our southwestern deserts has only 160 per square millimeter on both leaf surfaces. The opening and closing of stomates is influenced by light and water content of leaves, as well as temperature, but as a general rule they open during the day and close at night. When water is scarce, they close earlier in the day; during cool weather they remain closed.

Not all trees are able to close their stomates completely. Willows thrive only in moist places because they cannot close their stomates enough to prevent excessive moisture loss. On the other hand, aspens, which thrive best in moist situations, can also live in dry places because they can, if necessary, close their stomates completely.

Leaves have other tricks of conserving their vital water supply. Trees growing in dry situations sometimes turn their leaves on edge to avoid the hot sun. This can be seen in cottonwood seedlings. In some cases, especially in young leaves, the angle of leaves changes during the day as the sun gets hotter. The leaves of magnolia, privet and holly are protected from water loss by a thick outer skin or *cutin*. The curling up of leaves during periods of drought also helps them to conserve moisture.

The amount of water used by leaves and passed out through their stomates is quite remarkable. Even more remarkable, and somewhat baffling to scientists, is the ability of trees to lift this water from the soil to the tops of high branches. In the case of a Sequoia this may be nearly 300 feet. Scientists have learned to equip space ships with complex instruments and send them millions of miles into space, yet they do not fully understand how a tree "pulls" water up to its leaves. This would seem to be a simple thing, but it is not. There are, of course, several theories. It is known that water is absorbed into the roots by a process called *osmosis*, which results in root pressure. From the roots the water ascends through the trunk and limbs and finally enters

46

This cross-section of a wild grape vine, a typical woody stem, shows its many water ducts. (See photograph below.)

This photograph shows the great water-conducting capacity of a wild grape vine. A garden hose was attached to the end of the vine.

the leaves where about 10 per cent of it is used, the rest passing out of the stomates as vapor. Root pressure alone is not sufficient, however, to push water all the way up through the trunk of a tall tree to the leaves. Scientists know that other factors are involved. They have found that the leaves exert a very powerful pull on the millions of tiny columns of water flowing upward through the trunk. In some trees this water flows upward at the rate of 330 feet per hour. As you may know, a pump can *lift* water only about 33 feet. (It can, of course, *push* it much higher.) This is because the column of water below the pump breaks, forming a vacuum when the weight of the column becomes greater than one *atmosphere*. (An *atmosphere* is the pressure exerted by the air at sea level, and amounts to 14.7 pounds per square inch.) Amazingly, some scientists believe that a tree can lift a continuous column of water weighing 200 atmospheres. Such a column weighs about 293 pounds per square inch!

In order to solve the problem of water-lift in trees, scientists turned to a study of water itself. The molecules of water are very strongly attracted to each other and tend to stick together so that water will flow for some distance up a tiny glass tube without help. The walls of the xylem cells of the tree, through which the water is pulled upward, are readily wetted and there are no breaks. As a result, the minute columns of water tend to stick together so that the leaves can pull them upward. In this way, scientists believe, a tree is able to lift water to its highest leaves. The pressure supplied by the roots helps, but it is mostly the leaves which do the work of pumping water. In some trees, root pressure is more important than in others. Many trees and vines "bleed" as a result of root pressure when they are cut off near the ground—proof that water is also being forced up from below. This is true of birch, maple, box elder and others. Coniferous trees, such as pines, do not develop root pressure, however. Although scientists do not fully understand how a tree lifts water up to its leaves, the process by which manufactured foods are transported downward is understood even less.

The quantity of water used by trees is quite astounding. It is probable that, in temperate countries, the amount of water absorbed by plants is as great as that which flows down to the oceans in rivers. There are two ways of calculating the amount of water used by trees. One way is by determining how much water is needed to produce a pound of dry plant material. In the case of beech, it is estimated that 170 pounds of water are used in producing each pound of dry plant material. A birch requires more than twice this much water, as does an English oak. In general, most plants use from 200 to 500 pounds of water for each pound of plant produced. It has been calculated that a large apple tree having 100,000 leaves will use about four gallons of water an hour or 2,880 gallons per month. Different kinds of trees vary widely in their rates of water consumption. A red maple 53 feet tall was found to use six gallons a day or about 900 gallons during the growing season. Usually trees use more water during the day than during the night. Stomates or leaf pores close at night, cutting down the evaporation or transpiration of water. At night, of course, there is no sunshine and the leaves are not "working."

In order to obtain all this water a tree must have a very efficient root system. The roots of a tree branch and rebranch, ending at last in fine root hairs. Root hairs are in direct contact with soil particles, and it is chiefly through them that water is absorbed. They are very delicate structures that have short lives, most of them lasting but a few days or a few weeks. In the cases of such trees as redbud, Kentucky coffee trees and honey locust, the root hairs may last for several months. The total lengths of the root systems of plants vary greatly, depending on whether the plant is growing in a dry or moist habitat. Some trees and plants have shallow root systems, while the roots of others reach down to great depths, sometimes as much as 30 feet. Tree roots

The roots of a tree penetrate the ground to great depths to absorb water and minerals. These are the roots of a large magnolia.

have two functions; they anchor the tree to the ground and absorb water and dissolved minerals which are passed upward to the all-important leaves. If all the roots of a tree could be placed end to end the result would be quite amazing. Those of a large tree would certainly be many miles, and if the total root length of a Big Tree Sequoia 30 feet in diameter could be joined end to end they would probably reach around the world!

Leaves must be designed for survival as well as for the work they must do. Most leaves have long leaf-stalks or *petioles* that allow the blades to twist with the wind and rain. Solidly anchored leaves would soon be torn to bits. This movement in winds and breezes also allows light to penetrate into the darker interior of the tree. Incidentally, it also adds to their attractiveness. A quaking aspen with all its silvery leaves trembling in the breeze is, indeed, a pretty sight. The trembling of aspen leaves also has another advantage. It causes more water to pass out of the leaves. This might seem to be a disadvantage, but, actually, the water that passes up to the leaves from the roots carries dissolved minerals which are needed. The water passes out of the leaves, while the minerals are retained. Usually, too, aspens grow in places where moisture is abundant, so water loss is no problem. In one experiment it was found that when an aspen leaf was held still the amount of water that passed out was cut in half.

The shapes of most leaves are a little difficult to explain on a logical basis. Leaf shape is, of course, most important to us when we set out to identify a tree. Like fingerprints, no two kinds are ever alike. Some leaves, such as those of elms, are *asymmetrical*. That is, the two sides of the leaves are unequal in size. Botanists believe that this causes the leaves to tilt sideways in the rain, allowing water to drain off quickly. If you will examine a number of different leaves, you will find, also, that a large majority

Leaves of black or red oaks have sharp points. The white oaks have rounded lobes.

have sharp points at their outer ends or along their margins. You can see these "drop points" or "drip tips" in red oaks, willows, birches, poplars, hollies and many other trees. When rain falls upon a leaf it is important that it runs off as quickly as possible. Drops of water remaining on a leaf favor bacterial or fungal infection, and the leaf may even be injured by the lenslike droplets focusing the sun's rays on it. The "drip tips" cause the water to flow off the leaf quickly. As might be expected, the leaves of trees native to drier localities tend to have smooth margins. Water evaporates quickly, making "drip tips" unnecessary. The crown leaves of the quaking aspen are usually without "drip tips." Due to their continuous motion in the breeze, droplets of water are soon shaken off. And the leaves of seedling aspens are so arranged that rain falling on them soon flows down their petioles or drips off the short tips. This adaptation is necessary because the small trees are nearer the ground where there is less air movement and higher humidity.

Many leaves, such as those of oaks, are lobed or divided. In other cases, as in ash, locust and buckeye, the leaves are divided into many small leaflets. This increases their interest and attractiveness, of course, but there are very practical reasons for such arrangements, too. Large leaves of solid form are more apt to be frayed by winds while smaller leaves, or those of broken outline, allow winds to pass through without injuring them. But there is still another, and perhaps more important, advantage in broken outlines. The greater the margin of a leaf the more water it can evaporate and the more efficiently it can "breathe" in the carbon dioxide gas it needs. In a living leaf, a layer of water vapor builds up on the surface and flows down over its edges. The more and longer the edges of the leaf, the faster does this vapor flow off. Thus, leaves having broken outlines work more efficiently than leaves of solid form.

The fine teeth found along the margins of many leaves, such as hackberry and beech, are not a result of chance but have a

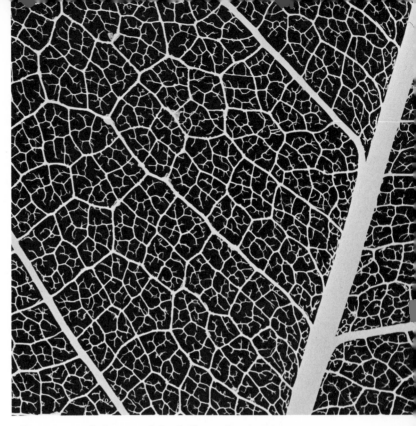

Close-up of skeletonized leaf shows how veins go to every part of a leaf, carrying water to its cells and manufactured foods away. The mid-rib is at right.

practical function. There are emergency water pores at these points that allow excess water to flow out of the leaf. You can sometimes see these tiny droplets suspended in rows along leaf margins on damp mornings. The loss of water in this way is called *guttation*.

So far we have said nothing about leaf veins. These appear as raised ridges that extend across, or form networks, on all tree leaves. Inside these veins there are fine ducts that carry water and minerals to the various parts of the leaf and manufactured sugars away. Each kind of leaf has its own particular type of vein pattern or *venation*. Maple, sweetgum and sycamore leaves are said to have palmate venation; the large veins all arise at the base of the leaf and spread out fanlike across the blade. Other leaves, such as those of the oak, elm, catalpa, basswood, poplar and birch, have a midrib or central vein extending from base to tip and smaller veins arising along each side. This is called *pinnate* venation. While these leaf veins have, as their principal function, the transportation of water and food, they also form a framework to stiffen the leaf.

In addition to the remarkable variation in leaf shape, there is the matter of leaf arrangement or *phyllotaxy*. You may think that the ways in which tree, or other, leaves are placed on twigs is more or less accidental or by chance, but leaf arrangements follow very precise and definite patterns predetermined by genetic or inherited factors. Botanists consider that there are three basic styles of leaf arrangement. Some leaves arise *opposite* each other on the twigs, as in dogwood, box elder and fringetree. In other trees, such as catalpa, several leaves arise at each point or node on the twigs in a *whorled* arrangement. By far the most common leaf arrangement, however, is the *spiral*. In this type the bases of the leaves are arranged in spirals up the stems and these spirals are of various types. They are the same spiral patterns found in tree limbs as discussed in an earlier chapter.

Leaves, as we have seen, are an important part of every tree. Yet they are temporary structures, used for a time and then discarded like old, worn-out clothing. In their living processes leaves gradually accumulate waste materials and wear out. Insects eat holes in them and fungi destroy their tissues. In northern climates, winter's cold kills many kinds. But even in tropical lands where the breath of winter is never felt, leaves are periodically discarded and replaced. There are both long-lived and short-lived leaves. Some live for only a few months while others live and carry on their work for several years. In our northern climate, trees that lose their leaves each autumn are called *deciduous* trees. This includes the aspens, maples, oaks, elms, larches and many others. Trees that keep their foliage all winter are called *evergreens*, examples being pines, spruces, magnolias and hollies.

54

At summer's end, leaves become worn out and are ready to be discarded.

You may think that the leaves of deciduous trees merely freeze and drop off in autumn. Actually, it is much more complicated than that. The fall of a leaf is the end result of a very orderly process. Trees are very economical. As autumn approaches and the time arrives for a tree to drop its leaves, about 90 per cent of the minerals in the leaves are transported out of them and stored in the tree's tissues. We might say that a tree actually cuts its leaves off when they are no longer necessary. Leaves remain attached to their twigs as long as they are busy manufacturing foods for the tree, but, at summer's end, or if they are injured in any way, the tree discards them. Injury may include damage caused by unfavorable temperature, deficient water supply, damage by insects or other factors. During times of extreme drought trees also drop their leaves. This helps the tree to conserve water. A layer of corklike cells gradually forms across the base of the leaf stem or petiole. This is called an *abscission* layer, which means "to cut off." The leaf then breaks away and falls. A healthy leaf continually produces a chemical regulator or auxin that prevents the formation of the abscission layer. An old or injured leaf does not produce enough of this auxin to prevent the formation of the break-away layer. There must, thus, be a continuous supply of auxin if the leaf is to remain on the tree.

The life of deciduous tree leaves in temperate climates is governed by the season. Most leaves unfold in April or May and remain on the trees until autumn, a period of about six months. The leaves of evergreens, on the other hand, last a long while. Holly leaves of various kinds live from 2 to 4 years. The life of pine needles (leaves) varies from 2 to 8 years, but, in most cases, pine needles are shed after about two years. The needles of some firs probably remain on the trees for as long as 12 years.

To those who admire trees, autumn is the season when they are dressed in their most beautiful raiments. It is in the cool climates of America, Europe and Asia, however, that autumn colors are especially enjoyed. The brilliant hues of sumacs, maples, oaks and other trees are due to the presence of several complex chemical pigments. First, there are the *carotenoids*, consisting of *carotenes* and *xanthophylls*, that give red or yellow

Leaf scar of hickory   *Leaf scar of sumac*

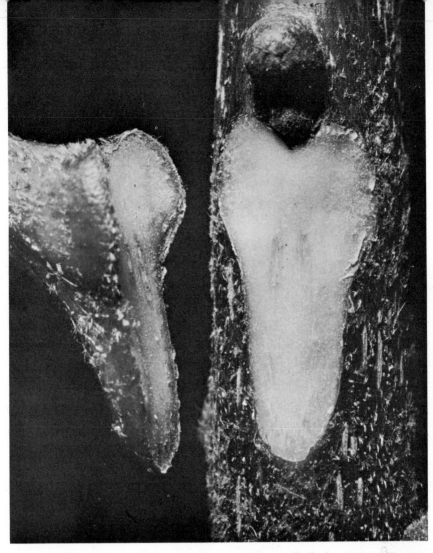

Leaves separate from the twigs by a process called abscission. *Here is shown a leaf separating from its twig. A leaf scar is left on the twig, and many trees can be identified in winter by their leaf scars alone.*

coloration to many trees such as tulip poplar, aspen and birch. Other pigments are the *anthocyanins,* ranging in color from scarlet to deep blue and purple. Anthocyanins are responsible for some of the most brilliant autumn coloration, including that of sumac, dogwood, beech and oak. At summer's end most leaves in our climate are of no further use to the trees, yet it is then that they assume their prettiest colors and when we enjoy them most.

The cottonwood has male and female trees. At left are female catkins from a female tree. At right are male or pollen-bearing catkins from a male tree.

CHAPTER 4

Trees and Their Flowers

Trees first began producing flowers many millions of years ago. Flowers are essential to seed production, without which most trees could not continue to reproduce themselves. To most of us the term "flower" means a bloom like that of the peach or magnolia, but many tree flowers—those of willows, oaks, hickories and birches, for example—are quite inconspicuous and are seldom noticed. The flowers of these trees are in the form of catkins or other structures without colorful petals. These may not agree with our ideas of flowers, yet they are actually simple flowers as truly as a rose or a buttercup. Such tree flowers do not have bright colors to attract insects; they must depend on the vagaries of winds to carry their pollen. In many ways, wind pollination is more primitive than insect pollination and was in style long before there were bees, butterflies or moths. Colored flowers were developed to attract insects, and without insects such blooms would be useless to trees and other plants.

In the scheme of Nature, a tree, during its life, has but one true aim: the production of seeds to assure the continuation of the species. All of a tree's life processes are pointed in this direction from the time it sprouts from the seed to the distant day when it dies and crashes to the earth. Each year most trees normally bloom and produce seeds, but the buds that produce flowers are usually produced the previous year. Thus, there is often a period of many months between the time of bud formation and the opening of the flower. For example, the dogwood forms its flower buds in late summer and these remain dormant all winter. Life within them remains quiet, waiting for warm weather and the rains of early spring. At that time the buds begin to grow and expand and the white "petals" or bracts unfold. In regions where dogwoods abound, the dreary winter woods are suddenly enlivened with snowy masses of flowers. This is the beginning of the pageant of spring. It will shortly be followed by millions of unfolding leaves and all the wonderful events of another summer. Apple trees produce their flower buds in early summer, but these will not open until the following spring. In the case of pines, pollination occurs in early spring but there is an entire year's delay in fertilization, and seeds are not actually produced until the third year, or even later. Strangely, a few trees and shrubs bloom during warm periods in winter before there is any sign of spring. Examples are witch hazel and alder. A number of fruit trees, including apple, orange, plum, olive and coffee, often flower and bear fruit abundantly only on alternate years. This same thing occurs in some forest trees.

The formation of flower buds is the first step in the production of flowers. Just what it is that stimulates the twigs to produce flowers is not fully understood by biologists. It is believed that the leaves secrete a special chemical regulator or auxin which flows to the growing tips of the twigs and causes them to begin the production of flowers. While biologists do not know just what this chemical regulator is, they have extracted it from plants and given it a name—"florigen." When this florigen is applied to the leaves of plants at seasons when they do not normally bloom, they soon start the formation of flowers.

There are many things that have an effect on tree flowering. To produce blooms a tree must first accumulate a supply of food materials in the form of starches and sugars. Apparently, florigen is then produced, which brings about the chain of events leading to the flower. The accumulation of foods by the growing tree depends on several external factors. These include the amount and kind of light reaching the leaves, the availability of moisture, and the amounts of mineral elements in the soil. The most important minerals are nitrogen, phosphorus and potassium. Nitrogen is probably the most important since it tends to govern the use of starch and sugar by the growing tree. The health of the trees is also important; a diseased tree does not usually produce many blooms. Sun-loving trees growing in deep shade will not usually bloom.

The flowering of most small plants is governed by the length of the days, or the *photoperiod*. Some plants are *short-day* plants that bloom in autumn or in spring when the days are short. Other plants are *long-day* plants because they bloom in midsummer while the days are long. And some plants are not affected by day length and so they are called *day-neutral* plants. This sensitivity to day length is an inherited trait and cannot be changed. Most trees, however, are not influenced much by day length; other factors seem to be more important. There are a few exceptions. Dogwood is considered to be a short-day tree, while some kinds of elms do not begin their flowering process until the arrival of the long-day condition of midsummer.

It has been found that anything which stops the downward flow of manufactured food materials through the phloem zone and away from the twigs will stimulate flower formation and fruiting. If a tree is girdled by cutting through the phloem zone, flowering is stimulated. The tree will, of course, eventually die. I have seen girdled magnolia trees bloom profusely for two years before they died. Peasants in certain European countries take advantage of this without knowing the scientific reasons. During a certain spring feast day they beat their fruit trees with clubs. This injures the phloem zones of the trees and apparently causes them to bear fruit more abundantly. Fortunately, the trees re-

This is the bloom of a tulip poplar tree. At the center are the pistils *or female parts of the flower, surrounded by a circle of* stamens, *the male parts, containing pollen. Enclosing these are the colorful* petals, *and deep within the throat are* nectar glands. *These flowers are pollinated by bees.*

cover from this beating and, after producing fruit, go on growing normally. There is an old folk saying that goes thus:

> Dogs and trees—
> The more you beat 'em
> The better they be.

Flowers come in many forms and tree flowers are no exception. A complete or *perfect* flower, one containing all the essential parts, is found in trees such as the tulip poplar. At the center is a cone made up of the pistil or pistils, containing the ovary with its immature seeds and the column called the style, at the top of which is the stigma where pollen is deposited for pollination. These are the female flower parts. Surrounding them are the male parts or stamens, each bearing an anther at the tip from which pollen is liberated to germinate on the female stigma and send pollen tubes down into the ovary where seeds are produced. Nectar glands that attract insects may be located near the base of the anthers, and the whole is surrounded by the petals—often very colorful—which make up the floral envelope. This in turn may be enclosed in leaflike sepals which form the calyx.

In wind-pollinated trees, such as oaks, hickories, cottonwoods, ashes, pines and willows, the petals are absent and the male and female parts are borne on separate twigs or even on separate trees. Such flowers are said to be *imperfect* because they lack either male or female parts. Trees having male and female organs on separate trees are more or less like animals in this respect; that is, the trees are either male or female. This condition is found in cottonwood, poplar, willow, holly, sassafras, persimmon, ginkgo, mulberry, Osage orange and some maples. In this way Nature makes sure that *cross-pollination*, or pollination between separate trees will occur. In most other trees or plants having both male and female flowers on the same individual,

These are the strange, deep purple blooms of the pawpaw.

Willows make self-pollination impossible by having their male and female flowers on separate trees. In this photograph, male catkins are at the left, and female catkins at the right.

self-pollination is possible. It is a great advantage to trees—as it is to other plants—to obtain cross-pollination, however. Cross-pollination results in better and more seed and, over many generations, more vigor and adaptability of the race.

The male flowers of wind-pollinated trees are most often in the form of catkins that hang suspended from the twigs. Usually they are seen in spring. The female flowers, on the other hand, are often quite small and inconspicuous and seldom seen by the average person. In a few trees, such as cottonwoods and willows, the female flowers are catkin-like.

Any breeze that causes the mature catkins to swing about brings down a golden shower of pollen that floats away. Most of the pollen of wind-pollinated trees is wasted since it falls on the ground or sticks to twigs. Out of the billions of pollen grains produced by a tree, only a very few ever alight upon their des-

These are the flowers of the sweet gum tree: male, above, and female, below. Here there is no provision to prevent pollen from falling upon the female flower of the same tree, as in the case of alder and other trees.

tined place—the pistil of a female flower of the same kind of tree, where germination can take place. Thus, wind pollination is very wasteful. But the production of numerous pollen grains is Nature's way of insuring the continuation of those trees that depend on the vagaries of the wind.

Generally speaking, trees that depend on wind for pollen transportation bloom in late winter or early spring before leaves are out. Of course, there are exceptions. Fully expanded leaves interfere with wind-borne pollen, large amounts adhering to the leaves where it is wasted. When limbs are bare the flying pollen grains can more easily reach their destinations on other flowers. Oaks liberate their pollen just as their leaves begin to unfold.

Pollen grains, when seen under a microscope, are like tiny jewels and range in form from perfect spheres to stars with sharp points in geometric designs. Within each tiny speck of

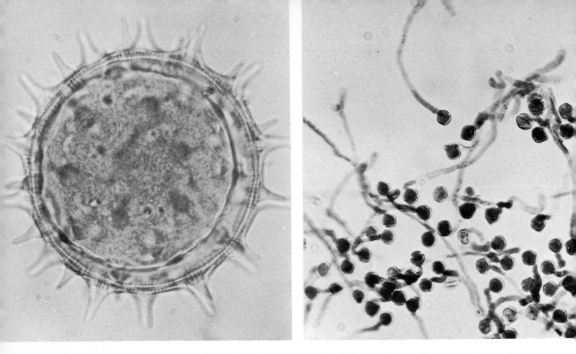

At left, a greatly enlarged pollen grain. At right, pollen tubes growing out of pollen grains that have alighted on the stigma of a flower. The tubes penetrate the ovary and bring about fertilization of seeds.

living matter is contained the complete "blueprint" of the future tree. It is almost unbelievable that a microscopic pollen grain can contain all the plans for the proper growth of a forest giant such as a Sequoia or an oak, but each tree—like every other plant—has its own special pollen grains and these can be identified under the microscope. Most pollen grains are more or less spherical, but those of pine and other conifers have a pair of attached, air-filled bladders to give them buoyancy in the wind. Pine pollen has been found hundreds of miles at sea and even on top of the Greenland ice cap where it had drifted from the mainland of North America.

Wind-borne pollen grains are usually of medium size since these float best. Large grains are too heavy to float in air; they are designed for insect transport. On the other hand, extremely small pollen grains tend to stick together in clumps and, thus, are not well fitted for wind transportation. They, too, are usually carried by insects. It has been found that the best size for flying pollen grains is between 17 and 58 microns in diameter, invisible to the naked eye. The pollen of many common trees comes in the middle of this range; alder pollen grains, for example, measure about 30 microns. To float well in wind, pollen must be powdery and not stick together. That designed for insect transport is usually sticky, causing it to adhere to insects' bodies or be easily collected and carried in the pollen baskets on bees' legs.

There are several ways that wind-pollinated trees increase the chance of their pollen being deposited on the female flowers of other trees of their kind to bring about cross-pollination. In the case of alder, both male and female flowers are borne on the same twig, but the female flowers, which resemble tiny, red cones, are always situated several inches above the male or pollen-producing catkins at the tip of each twig. When the male catkins begin shedding pollen it floats away in the breeze and there is not much chance that it will alight on female cones on the same tree.

Many pines have a rather similar arrangement to reduce the chance of self-pollination and inbreeding. The female cones are higher on the tree than are the clusters of male cones. The yel-

At left, a female flower or cone of pine. At right, pine pollen grains. Each grain has two attached air-filled bladders (the dark areas shown here). Winds carry pine pollen grains which alight on the female cone and are drawn into small openings between the scales.

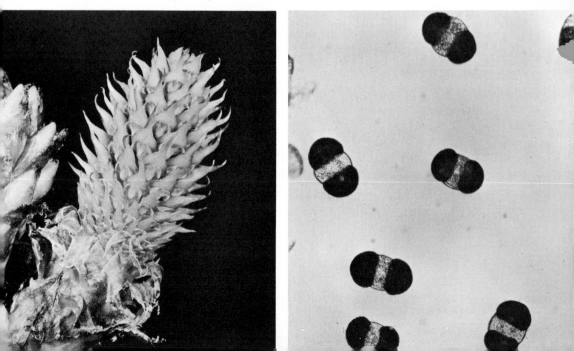

low pollen showers downward, but air currents tend to lift the drifting pollen high in the air where it alights on female cones of distant trees.

The actual pollination of pines is interesting and differs considerably from that of broad-leaf trees. Between each of the closely packed scales that make up the small female cone there is a tiny opening called a *micropyle* (meaning "little door"). When a pollen grain alights near a micropyle, it adheres to a droplet of sticky fluid. When this sticky fluid evaporates, the pollen grain is drawn into the micropyle where a pollen tube grows out of the pollen grain. Almost an entire year passes before fertilization or the actual union of the male and female cells occurs and the development of the seed-bearing cone commences. When the cone reaches maturity there are winged seeds between each scale. In time the scales dry out and separate, liberating the seeds which sail away in the wind. Thus, pine trees depend on winds for both pollen transport and seed dispersal.

A number of common trees make self-pollination impossible by having completely separate sexes. If you have wondered why some holly or mulberry trees never produce fruit, that is the reason. They are probably male trees. The easiest tree to observe in this respect is the cottonwood because it grows almost everywhere. If you will examine a number of cottonwoods in spring when they are in flower, you will find that there are two kinds of flowers. Some trees bear dense catkin masses that are yellow or reddish in color. These are the male or pollen-producing flowers, and the tree bearing them is a male. The flowers on female cottonwood trees are loose clusters of small flowers and are much less conspicuous than the male catkins. Cottonwood pollen is carried by the wind from male to female trees as is also the down-covered seed from which the tree gets its name.

Fortunately, for the beauty of our forests, many common trees bear flowers with large, colorful petals designed by Nature to

Alders have both sexes on the same tree, but prevent self-pollination by having the female flowers located above the male catkins.

attract insects for their help in carrying pollen. These include dogwood, tulip poplar, magnolia, catalpa and haw, as well as most fruit trees. Attractive blooms are present on many tropical forest trees, too. The flowers of these trees are typical blooms, complete with pistils, stamens, petals and nectar glands. They come in many forms; there are the pealike flowers of coral beans, yellow-wood and redbud, the spreading flowers of tulip poplar and magnolia, and the deep-throated blooms of catalpa, all of which are insect-pollinated. The colored petals of the flowers serve as advertising signs to lure the insects—the bees, butterflies and moths—but it is not a free service the flowers are asking; the insects are paid off in pollen and nectar. Many tree flowers produce nectar abundantly. In some regions beekeepers depend largely on tulip poplar as a source of nectar, which the bees carry back to their hives and manufacture into delicious honey. Fruit

69

trees are, of course, favorite nectar-producing trees, and bee-keepers in the coastal areas of western Florida, Mississippi and Louisiana value the titi or ironwood for its early spring nectar flow. In almost every part of the country there are flowering trees that contribute nectar to bees for the manufacture of honey. As a matter of fact, many beekeepers move their hives from one region to another, taking advantage of nectar-producing flowers that bloom with the season.

Tree flowers, like other flowers, are specialists, catering to certain kinds of insects. The locusts and tulip poplars depend on bees, as does the catalpa. The magnolia attracts beetles with its huge, white flower bowls. Most other white flowers open at night to attract night-flying moths.

Insect-pollinated trees also use various tricks to prevent or reduce the chance of self-pollination. In some cases pistils are poisonous to pollen from the same flower. In other cases pollen is liberated by the anthers before the stigmas of the same flower are ready to receive it. In the catalpa flower, the pollen-bearing anthers are located inside the flower tube while the stigma extends outward where it will be in the path of insect visitors. The tip of the stigma is split into two lips, one curving up and the other downward. Only the pollen grains deposited on the inside surfaces of the lips will germinate and bring about fertilization. Now suppose a bee comes to the catalpa bloom seeking the nectar hidden deep inside. As it enters, some of the pollen from previously visited blooms is rubbed off onto the lower lip of the stigma. The bee continues crawling on into the flower in search of nectar, where the anthers dust its back with a fresh supply of pollen. In the meantime, the stigma lips rapidly close together so that when the bee backs out of the flower none of the pollen grains that have just been dusted on its back can be rubbed off. The stigma lips of the catalpa flower are very sensitive, and, if touched with a needle, will rapidly close. Thus, has Nature designed the flower to prevent self-pollination.

When a bee visits a catalpa flower, pollen from other blooms is rubbed off on the forked stigma. But as the bee crawls on into the flower where it picks up pollen from the stamens, the stigma lips close so that none of the flower's own pollen can be rubbed off on its own stigma as the bee leaves.

Here the lips of a catalpa stigma have been touched with a pencil, causing them to close. This same thing occurs when the lips are touched by a bee entering the flower.

Seeds of slippery elm are shaped like discs, each with a
papery wing. Winds often carry them great distances.

The seeds of ash are also winged. As they are carried by
winds, their spinning motion slows down their fall.

CHAPTER 5

From Little Seeds

$\mathcal{A}$ tree must grow where its life begins—unless someone transplants it. Animals have legs, fins or wings and may travel great distances to establish themselves in new areas where life may be more favorable. Throughout their lives trees are anchored to the earth from which they obtain their nourishment and water. Still, trees have traveled to almost every land where climates would permit their growth. How did they travel? They sent their seeds. Seeds are packages of life that may be carried great distances. They are one of Nature's greatest miracles. An acorn, for example, is actually a tree complete in every detail, all wrapped up in a tiny, convenient package that may be carried about and eventually planted. Airborne seeds may even cross oceans before settling down at last to grow in the soil and many trees air-mail their seeds to distant places.

It is a great advantage for a seed to move away from the parent tree. If all the seeds from a tree should fall and grow directly under it, there would soon be a dense clump of seedlings struggling for space, none of which could ever mature. Nature prevents this overcrowding in many different ways. Some tree seeds are equipped with wings that slow up their fall, thus giving winds a chance to carry them considerable distances. Most of us are familiar with the winged seeds or "keys" of maples. These are produced in pairs, but when mature they

These are winged seeds of maple. As they fall, the attached wings cause them to spin, slowing their descent and allowing winds to carry them away.

break apart and fall from the tree. As they fall, however, they go into spiral spins and this spinning motion slows up their descent. In a breeze, maple seeds may be carried for several hundred yards before reaching the ground. The seeds of *Ailanthus* or tree-of-heaven are also winged, but they spin in a different manner. With thin wings extending from each end, they spin horizontally, and, as they fly through the air, they look very much like flying insects. Even a slight breeze may be sufficient to carry them a long way. Their seeds fly much more efficiently than those of maples.

Many other common trees equip their seeds with papery

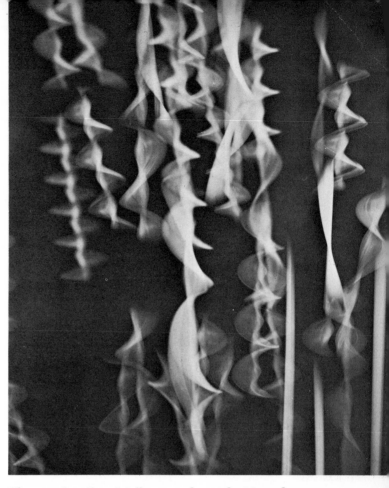

The spiral paths of falling maple seeds. Note the straight paths at lower right, made by seeds that failed to go into their spins and fell faster.

wings to enable at least a few of their descendants to reach favorable ground in distant locations. Examples are ash, catalpa and elm. Botanists call winged tree seeds *samaras*. Trees which depend on samaras for propagation usually produce an enormous number to offset the small chance of their falling on suitable soil. Another tree with flying seeds is the birch which sheds its seeds late in autumn. Still another is the hop hornbeam, whose seeds are enclosed in a cluster of leaflike bracts, which resembles the hop and from which it gets its name. Basswood, too, equips each of its seed clusters with a wing. The coconut tree produces enormous seeds, well-protected and stocked with food. Their chances of survival are good so the tree needs to produce only a few seeds or nuts. By contrast, an orchid seed's chance for life is extremely small; therefore, some orchids produce nearly four million dustlike seeds to each pod.

The tiny down-covered seeds of the willow and cottonwoods are familiar to all of us. At certain seasons the air in the vicinity of these trees is filled with drifting "cotton." The seeds of the cottonwood are especially interesting. If they settle on moist soil, such as the margin of a stream, they germinate within a few hours and begin putting out tiny green leaves. Nature wastes no time since the life of cottonwood seeds is very brief. Of course, very few of these germinating seeds actually grow into trees. If they all did grow, there would be no room in the world for any other kind of trees.

Many trees use water transportation to disperse their precious seed cargoes. Ocean currents and rivers flow quite rapidly, often covering great distances, and any floating object is carried along with them. Black currant seeds from Japan are washed up on Oregon beaches after drifting nearly half way around the world in the Japanese current. Cashew and mahogany seeds are also carried great distances by ocean currents. These currents follow definite paths over the earth and have undoubtedly had much to do with the distribution of trees and other plants. Coconut trees often grow along the margins of seas and usually lean out over the water. When the nuts fall they are carried away by the current. The outer covering is quite hard and resistant to water and the space between this covering and the nut proper is filled with fiber. The coconut is thus equipped with a very efficient "life jacket." It is believed that the original home of the coconut tree was the west coast of Central America, but it has now spread to almost all the lands and islands of the Tropics. It is not at all unusual to see large numbers of sprouting coconuts along the beaches of quiet estuaries of tropical islands. The seeds of other palms, too, are carried by ocean currents. One of

The seeds of willow and cottonwood are attached to masses of cottony fiber easily carried by winds. These are willow seeds.

these is the nipa palm, often used in thatching native huts. This palm grows with its trunk submerged so that only its long fronds are exposed. The seeds are often washed ashore along with all sorts of other seeds and debris tossed aside by the ocean.

The largest seed in the world is the double coconut or coco-de-mer, which weighs up to 60 pounds and is produced by a palm growing in interior valleys of the Seychelles Islands in the Indian Ocean. It is a large tree, often reaching heights of 90 or more feet, yet the huge nuts of this tree were known long before the tree itself was discovered. Two or three times the size of coconuts, they look like two coconuts joined side by side. They were sometimes found along the beaches of India, and sailors told many strange tales to explain their origin. Large sums were sometimes paid for these mysterious "nuts of the sea" in the belief that they had great curative power, especially in cases of poisoning. Even though these huge nuts often drift long distances from their native islands, they apparently do not germinate and grow after long submersion in the sea. Thus, the trees never became established in other places.

The berries of mistletoe contain sticky seeds which are carried on the beaks and feet of birds from one tree to another.

When the seeds of most trees fall upon suitable ground some of them eventually grow into trees in the usual way. There are, however, some interesting exceptions. Strangler figs or banyans occur in many tropical countries. The seeds of these remarkable trees germinate on the bark of other trees, sending their roots down over the surface of the trees to the ground. For a time the fig lives as a vine, but it eventually surrounds the host tree and strangles it, after which it puts down many more roots and slowly expands into a great, sprawling tree consisting of numerous trunks. In the humid forests of the Olympic Peninsula of Washington, hemlock seeds also germinate on the damp bark of other trees. The young tree lives upon the bark until it can send its roots down to anchor it to the soil. The seeds of mistletoe are sticky and are carried from tree to tree on birds' beaks and feet. They germinate on the bark, sending their "roots" or sinkers down into the wood to steal nourishment from the tree. Thus, mistletoes are parasites.

One of the world's most unusual trees is the mangrove, a small sprawling tree that inhabits the margins of many tropical seas, and thrives with its roots in salt water. It is common along the coasts of southern Florida where mangroves grow and multiply by putting out prop roots that curve out and down and take root. New stems arise as the tangled mass of vegetation continues to advance toward the sea, and because of their manner of growth they have been called "walking trees." These dense growths are almost impenetrable by any creature except snakes. As the prop roots reach out and anchor themselves to the bottom of the sea, they help to hold silt and, eventually, new land is formed through their assistance. The mangrove produces small, nodding flowers, and these in turn give rise to leathery brown fruits which germinate while still suspended from the tree, producing spearlike roots eight or ten inches long. These "loaded darts" have their thickest ends near the bottom, which is pointed, and eventually these root-spears fall from the tree, pierce the mud and begin growing. If the water beneath the tree is too deep for the root-spears to reach the mud, however, they bob back to the surface and float away in the current in a horizontal position. As the root-spears float along, the center of gravity slowly shifts so that they become heaviest at their bottom ends.

Mistletoe seeds germinate on the bark of trees and send "sinkers" into the living wood to obtain food. Here a tree limb with attached mistletoe has been sawed in half, showing the sinkers.

This causes them to swing to vertical positions with their points downward so that when they reach shallow water they stick in the mud and take root. In this way new mangrove thickets may arise along distant shores.

Nuts of most kinds, if they fall in the water, may float long distances before sprouting and growing into trees. These include the nuts of hickory, walnut, pecan, chestnut, and oak. Normally, however, these nuts fall to the ground and sprout where they fall. In many cases they are buried in autumn by squirrels or chipmunks who forget where some of their buried treasures were hidden. With the coming of spring these nuts start growing. Jays, too, pick up nuts and carry them away with the intention of opening them. A few are dropped and forgotten. Animals help disperse tree seeds in other ways, too. When eating apples, peaches or other fruit, it does not usually occur to us to wonder why the tree enclosed the seed or seeds in such delicious food. The truth is that Nature tricks us, as well as other animals, by hiding seeds inside edible fruit of many kinds so that they will be carried away and "planted." In the case of humans, an apple may be eaten and the core discarded, but the seeds may grow. The seeds of many kinds of fruit have hard coverings and may pass through the digestive systems of animals without injury. As a matter of fact, it has been found that some seeds, such as those of the barberry, actually germinate better after passing through animals' digestive systems! The same thing is probably true of persimmon seeds. A number of seeds, such as those of the yew tree, are brightly colored to attract birds or other animals.

Thus, a number of tricks are used by trees to assure that their seeds will grow in places some distance from the parent. Some of these, as we have seen, are quite clever, but none is as clever as that used by the witch hazel. Witch hazel blooms in autumn or late winter—which is unusual—and, by the following autumn, pods which have thick lips are produced. These lips

Oak acorns buried by squirrels or chipmunks are often forgotten and grow into trees.

When juniper burs open, their seeds fall to the ground or are carried away by birds.

gradually open and, in doing so, they exert considerable pressure on the seeds which rest between them. Eventually, sufficient pressure develops on the seeds to shoot them out of the pod. Some may be propelled eight or ten feet! This is similar to the way in which watermelon seeds may be snapped from between the thumb and finger.

Generally speaking, short-lived trees begin seed production sooner than long-lived kinds. For instance, short-lived trees such as aspens, birches and willows begin producing full crops of seed at ten to twenty years, while long-lived oaks and hickories do not begin full production until they are forty or fifty years old. In some trees there is a slow decline in seed production with old age, but some oaks continue to increase production as long as they remain growing and healthy.

Not all seeds remain alive and capable of germinating for the same length of time. Cottonwood seeds are short-lived while some pine seeds may germinate after 30 years. This difference is partly the result of the conditions under which they are kept and partly the result of genetic or inherited characteristics. Moisture, for example, has considerable effect on seed longevity (length of life). When the seeds of the silver maple are shed they contain about 58 per cent water, but the seeds die if their water content drops below 30 per cent. Sugar maple seeds, however, will still germinate when dried down to 5 per cent. Seeds which must survive the winter in cold climates usually contain less moisture than those of warm climates. The amount of fat stored in seeds also affects their cold resistance; the more fat the better they can withstand cold. A seed may look like a lifeless object, but it is a living, breathing thing. It is true that its life processes are greatly slowed down, yet delicate tests show that seeds are continually breathing or taking in oxygen and releasing carbon dioxide. Increasing the moisture content of a seed speeds up its living processes and causes it to use up its stored food. This, of course, shortens its life.

You may be surprised to learn that most seeds (about 70 per cent) are sensitive to light and will not germinate in darkness or dim light. It has been found that red light is especially important. On the other hand, the germination of a few plant seeds is slowed down or stopped by light. Birch seeds will not germinate in deep forest but will do so in open areas exposed to the sun. This is apparently because the red rays are absorbed by the leaves of the dense forest and do not reach the ground. Perhaps this is Nature's way of preventing the germination of birch seeds in dense forests where they would have difficulty in growing in competition with other trees. The seeds of the mistletoe, a para-

82

When this sweet gum "ball" swings in the wind it scatters its seeds. This is a green ball, before seeds have matured.

Beech seeds are triangular in shape, with two seeds in each bur.

site of many trees, are also unable to germinate in darkness. The seeds of some pines will germinate in dim light such as that found in open forest, but the seeds of the jack pines will germinate in complete darkness. This may be an adaptation to germination on the forest floor beneath the dense stands of these trees.

Temperatures also affect the lives of seeds. The seeds of many plants native to cold climates will not germinate until they have been exposed to low temperatures. This needed exposure may be very short or last for several months. Apple seeds, for example, must be kept at a temperature of about 38°F. for at least two months before they will germinate. The short life of cottonwood and willow seed under natural conditions has already been mentioned. If, however, these seeds are kept at low temperatures, they will live much longer. The same thing is true of aspen seeds. There are some cases where an "after-ripening" period is needed before germination will take place, a condition important to many seeds from the standpoint of survival. If seeds germinated immediately after they fell from the trees in summer, most of the young, tender seedlings would be killed by the cold weather of winter.

How long seeds will remain alive and able to germinate is a subject that has interested scientists for a long while. Numerous experiments have been carried out in which it has been found that many weed seeds may live 60 or 70 years. As a general rule, long-lived seeds are usually those that are larger than average and have smooth, hard coats. They will not swell when submersed in water. Seeds usually remain alive longest when stored under fairly dry conditions at rather low temperatures. Most dry seeds can stand great extremes of temperature. For example, dry lotus seeds still germinated after being placed in water slightly above the boiling point for sixteen hours. As a matter of fact, the seeds of the Indian lotus—a water lily—are believed to be the longest lived of any seed. They have germinated after being buried in a dry lake bed in Manchuria for a thousand years! Their true age was determined by modern radio-carbon methods. Germination of these remarkable seeds was obtained by first soaking them in concentrated sulfuric acid, which is so powerful that it will quickly dissolve most any other plant material. The seeds of many trees, such as those of birch, beech and elm, remain capable of germination only until the following spring.

The germination and growth of a seed into a new plant is one of the real miracles of nature. Proper conditions of moisture, temperature and light must be present before seeds will begin growing. Probably the most important factor is adequate moisture. At first the developing plant is completely dependent upon food stored in the seed by the parent tree, but, as growth continues, this food is slowly used up. In time the seed and the embryo tree growing out of it may weigh only half as much as the original seed. Green leaves eventually unfold, however, and begin their lifelong work of manufacturing food with the aid of the sun. From that time on the young tree is self-sufficient and another link has been added to the endless chain of life reaching out of the past and into the future. The destiny of the seed has been fulfilled.

This is a close-up of germinating cottonwood seeds only a few hours after falling on wet sand. These seeds germinate very rapidly.

The end of a fossilized log that grew in the Mississippi Valley many millions of years ago.

CHAPTER 6

Tree Rings — Keys to the Past

*P*eriodically, we read about someone sealing a collection of documents and other objects representative of our present age in a stainless steel container which is then deeply buried in the ground with appropriate ceremonies. It is presumed that these "time capsules," as they are called, will be dug up at some far distant day and give the discoverers information about our lives and culture. Thus do we attempt to communicate with those who will follow us thousands of years in the future.

Nature herself has been burying "time capsules" for many millions of years. These are in the form of plant and animal fossils that have been preserved in ancient lake and river sediments. As the eons passed, the sediments, along with the fossils they contained, slowly turned to stone. These records preserved in stone tell us much about the plants, animals and even the climates of those ancient days. But the fossils, themselves, do not tell us how old they are. In order to find this out scientists must employ special techniques, but these are complicated and not very accurate in dating fossils that are very old. Gradually better methods are being developed and dead plant and animal remains only a few thousand years old can be dated quite accurately. The most commonly used dating method at present is that using Carbon[14] or radio-carbon. Radio-carbon atoms are radioactive and are formed in the air by the bombardment of nitrogen atoms by cosmic rays. These radio-carbon atoms combine with oxygen atoms in the air to form carbon dioxide gas. This gas is absorbed by living plants and stored in their tissues. Animals in turn eat the plants so that their bodies, too, contain these Carbon[14] atoms. These atoms are unstable and change very slowly back into nitrogen. When a plant or animal dies, the radio-carbon atoms it contains begin the change back into nitrogen. This change occurs at a very definite rate. It is an atomic clock that slowly ticks off the years. In 5,568 years half of the radio-carbon atoms will disappear, having been changed back into nitrogen. This is called the "half life." The change goes on indefinitely so that during the next 5,568 years the amount of radio-carbon is cut in half again, and so on. This atomic clock goes ticking on regardless of what happens to the plant or animal remains that contain the radioactive carbon atoms. Since the rate of "decay" of the carbon atoms is known, it is possible for scientists to determine, within a few years, how long a plant or animal has been dead, or rather how long ago it lived. This is the "radio-carbon dating" that has enabled archeologists to determine how long ago many things were alive and growing, including such things as wood and bone fragments, peat from peat beds, and grain stored in ancient grain bins. In this way, too, scientists have been able to determine the ages of the various ancient civilizations of Egypt and other localities, as well as the ages of American Indian relics. It has been found also that the Ice Age began in northern United States about 9,000 B.C., since it was then that the forests there were destroyed by the advancing ice sheet. A short time ago scientists discovered the sites of ancient campfires near Las Vegas, Nevada. Charcoal from these fires was dated by radio-carbon methods and found to be about 30,000 years old, proving that humans have lived in North America far longer than previously suspected.

Thus, radio-carbon dating has been of great aid to scientists. Unfortunately, however, it is possible to determine the ages of

By counting a tree's annual growth rings its age can be determined quite accurately. This tree was about 75 years old.

ancient plant and animal remains back only to about 30,000 years. There are other atomic methods of dating, such as the potassium-argon method, that make possible the approximate dating of plant and animal remains that are many millions of years old. But these "atomic clocks" only achieve an accuracy of plus or minus a few years. This, of course, is close enough for most purposes, but scientists always strive for complete accuracy. This is where the "diaries" that have been kept by trees for thousands of years come in handy. These tree "diaries" are in the form of yearly growth rings and are very valuable to scientists even though they only go back about two thousand years.

The story of tree-ring dating began in the year 1901 when A. E. Douglass, then a young assistant astronomer at the Lowell Observatory in Arizona, was riding through a pine forest. Dr. Douglass was not a forester or even a botanist; actually, he was interested in sunspots. Scientists believed that these mysterious spots that appeared now and then on the sun's disc occurred in cycles; that is, that there were years when the spots were especially abundant and that these years alternated with years when sunspots were few. The periods of peak sunspot abundance were, it was believed, about eleven years apart. It was also suspected that they had some effect on weather and corresponded to moisture or rain cycles.

As Dr. Douglass rode through the Arizona forest, it occurred to him that the answers he sought regarding sunspot cycles and their influence on weather might be found recorded in the growth rings of the pines. It was most fortunate that Dr. Douglass was located in Arizona and that the first trees he studied were ponderosa pines. These trees are now known to be one of the best kinds for such studies. It was lucky also that he began his studies in this semi-desert region because only in such regions are trees so sensitive to fluctuations in weather from year to year. In comparing the yearly growth rings of various individual ponderosa pines Dr. Douglass soon found that the widths of their growth rings for the same years were similar. In other words, each year the individual trees grew about the same amount. This was the first step. Dr. Douglass next obtained rainfall records of previous years and found that during years of abundant rain the growth rings were wide, while during years of deficient rain the growth rings were narrow. In this dry region all trees live in a state of delicate balance with respect to the availability of moisture.

As the years passed, Dr. Douglass continued his studies of weather in relation to tree growth. He collected data from other parts of North America and from Europe. By 1915 he had established beyond doubt that the widths of the growth rings did follow the sunspot cycles of 11.5 years. The matter of tree growth is very complicated and is still not fully understood. In some regions tree growth depends on rainfall, but in others rain is not so important. The growth of a tree as recorded in its rings is

90

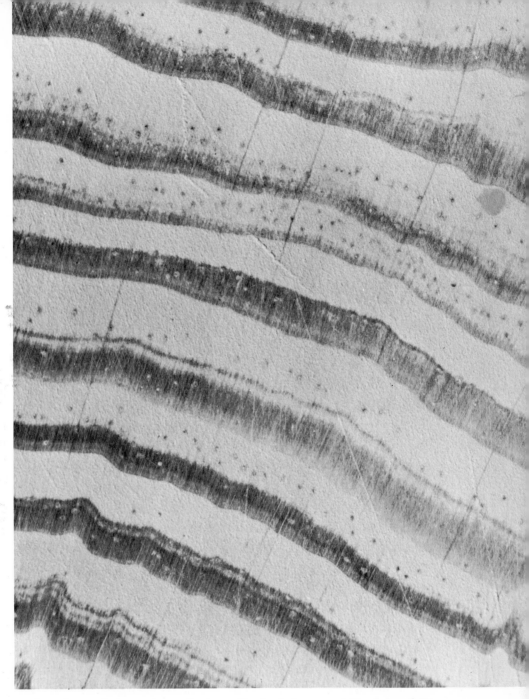

In this close-up of pine growth rings, the bark is toward the lower left. The white portions represent rapid spring growth; the dark lines represent slow summer growth. Eight years of growth are shown. Some of the dark summer rings are interrupted by spurts of late growth (see bottom left), probably caused by heavy rains. Thus, tree rings contain weather records.

affected by many things. These include altitude, latitude (distance north or south from the equator), temperature, and last, but not least, moisture. In many cases there are "false" rings to further confuse the issue. Sometimes early frosts bring summer growth to an abrupt stop but the growth starts again with the return of warm weather. Such an occurrence is faithfully recorded in the growth rings and appears like *two* seasons' growth. The same thing may occur when a tree is defoliated by insects or diseases. Growth stops and then starts again as the tree struggles to put out a new leaf canopy. In some areas, such as West Texas, the formation of false rings each summer is characteristic, and during a very dry year, a tree may skip a year in its growth-ring record. It can be seen that tree-ring dating is often quite complicated and can lead to false conclusions if the scientists are not careful.

In spite of all these difficulties, however, Dr. Douglass was able to prove that tree rings could be used to study sunspot cycles. The trees he found most useful for this work were ponderosa pine and Douglas fir. Using the oldest trees he could find, Dr. Douglass was able to trace sunspot cycles back only about 348 years. This was the average age of the living ponderosa pines he studied. The next step in the story began when the principle of cross-dating was discovered. Dr. Douglass and his assistants were lucky in finding many beams in old Indian pueblos that could be studied. Soon it was discovered that some of the latest growth rings in these beams matched the oldest rings in recently cut trees. The records, thus, lapped over each other and extended the record further back in time. More searches revealed other and older pueblo beams that could be cross-dated, extending the record back even further. In studying these growth-ring records it was not usually necessary to saw off the beams. An instrument called an *increment* borer was used. With this instrument a pencil-sized core from a beam or tree can be extracted for study.

An increment borer being twisted into a pine tree. (See photographs on page 95.)

The task of collecting wood beams and timbers from the ancient dwellings was tremendous. Even more painstaking was the work of matching and fitting the tree-ring records into a continuous calendar. This was eventually done, using not only the beams and other fragments of wood from the ancient pueblos but charred logs and timbers and even pieces of charcoal. In this way the record was pushed back, step by step, to the year 1260. It was scientific detective work of the most precise kind.

During the task of collecting the wood samples, a continuous record of tree rings that seemed even more ancient had been pieced together. This covered a period of 551 years and seemed very old, but it could not be fitted onto the continuous record that had already been established back to 1260. Where did it belong? It was not until 1929 that Dr. Douglass found a charred log in an ancient Indian dwelling at Showlow, Arizona, that supplied the "missing link." This log had started growth in 1237 and had been cut in 1380. When its growth rings were studied, it was found that they bridged the gap between the record that went back to 1260 and the 551-year record, and joined them together into a continuous year-by-year record of tree rings extending back to the year 709 A.D. Since that time this southwestern record has been pushed back to the year 11 A.D., giving us a continuous record of tree growth for over 1900 years! This study of tree-ring dating, by the way, has now become an important branch of science. It is called *dendrochronology.*

Trees in other places have been used in growth-ring studies, and some of these take us even further back in time than the Arizona pines. In some cases the entire spread in time for several thousand years back can be traced in individual trees. The huge General Sherman Sequoia in California is believed to be about 3,500 years old. No one knows for sure how old it really is because it is protected and cannot be cut down and no boring instrument is long enough to reach its center, even if the National Park Service would permit its use. Other ancient Sequoias have been cut and their long tree-ring records studied.

Recently, it was found that bristlecone pines growing on the White Mountains of California are also very old. They grow very slowly in the arid highlands and are twisted and deformed by the inhospitable climate. They do not grow to large size, yet borings in their trunks have proven them to be very ancient. In fact, some of them may be 4,000 years old—even older, perhaps, than the great Sequoias.

You may have wondered why it is important for us to have detailed information on past climates and sunspot activity. This information has great practical importance, for it is only through a knowledge of past climatic changes that we can predict future climates and weather conditions. Trees have thus supplied scientists with a means of looking into the future. In his studies of sunspot cycles and their effect on tree growth, Dr. Douglass discovered some very remarkable things. Previous to the completion of the 1900-year calendar there were no reliable records of

Core of wood showing growth rings extracted from increment borer. By use of this instrument growth rings can be seen without actually cutting down the tree.

These are cores cut from trees by means of an increment borer. Note how rates of growth vary in trees growing in different locations.

sunspots going back more than a hundred years. This was not long enough for scientists to determine if there were greater cycles over long periods of time. It is now known, as a result of the tree-ring research, that, in addition to the 11.5-year sunspot cycle, there is also a longer, 500-year cycle. In other words, there are sunspot cycles within sunspot cycles. Also revealed by the tree rings is the fact that there was a period between 1650 and 1720 when sunspots disappeared. Why this occurred no one knows. It is one of those mysteries out of the past that may never be explained. Old records kept at the Royal Observatory at Greenwich, England, indicated that few sunspots were seen from 1645 to 1715. These dates correspond closely to the tree-ring record and tend to prove that it is reliable.

The tree rings also tell us a number of other things. For instance, about every hundred years there occur about fifteen rings that are four or five times the width of the others. This indicates that during those years the rainfall was very heavy. We learn also from the tree-ring calendar that during the year 800 A.D. there were unusually heavy rains. There are also some unsolved mysteries in this detective story. The rings produced by many trees during the year 1580 are strongly distorted, and some trees produced no growth rings at all during that year. What happened? We do not know.

We may perhaps find a clue in something that happened in 1816. This was the so-called "year without a summer." During this summer the ground remained frozen in northern United States so that crops could not be planted. Low temperatures during midsummer occurred as far south as Georgia, and there were killing frosts for eight consecutive nights in Boston during June. There were no crops harvested in many parts of the country. It was only later that the explanation was discovered. A volcanic eruption had exploded the mile-high top off of Mount Timbora on Sumbawa Island, one of the Sunda Islands in the East Indies. Fifty-six thousand people were killed and millions of tons of dust were blown into the sky. This dust drifted into the upper atmosphere and formed a blanket around the earth which prevented the sun's heat from reaching it. Perhaps something similar occurred during the mystery year of 1580.

According to the tree-ring calendar, there was a great drought that lasted from 1276 to 1299. If we examine the calendar record even further back in time, as recorded in the rings of the California Sequoias, we find that there was an even greater drought about 1200 B.C. It lasted a hundred years and seems to have extended around the world, for if we turn to the written records of the Old World, we find this drought recorded there also. In Asia it was a time of famine. Desert tribes were forced to seek new living areas in order to survive. In the First Book of Kings we find the Biblical story of the great famine in the days of the Prophet Elijah. We find also that during this time Joseph was teaching the Egyptians to store up their food during good years in order to survive the lean years of drought.

Tree-ring dating has been of great value to scientists in another way. The ancient Indian pueblos or villages of the Southwest were the sources of many of the beams and timbers that enabled Dr. Douglass and his assistants to compile the continuous record back to the year 11 A.D. But the dating of the beams and timbers also determined the probable year when the pueblos were built. These dates are only approximate since wooden beams do not decay rapidly in the dry climate and could be used over and over for constructing dwellings. One timber was found that had probably been in use for at least 500 years!

The dating of ancient dwelling places by the use of tree-ring studies has also been carried out in Egypt and other countries. The ages of pieces of driftwood from old Eskimo villages have been determined. Five different Eskimo dwelling sites have now been dated, covering a period of a thousand years. Some scientists believe that radio-carbon dating may eventually replace tree-ring dating, but there will still be a place for the tree-ring calendar because its dates are precise and can be determined to the exact year.

Thus we see that, in addition to their other uses to mankind, trees also help us to unravel the secrets of the past and, perhaps, even to peer into the future. A tree's memories are recorded in its rings.

Old trees have a special appeal to us. Perhaps this is because they appear to be almost immortal as compared to our own relatively short lives. A person who reaches the age of a century is considered very ancient indeed, but many 100-year-old trees are still in their infancy. Time in its passing seems to leave some trees almost untouched. We gaze in awe at the great Egyptian Pyramids because they are some 4,000 years old. Yet some of the great Sequoias of California and the dragon trees of the Canary Islands are just as old, or perhaps older. The bristlecone pines mentioned previously may also reach the 4,000-year mark. Actually, there is no reason to believe that trees like the Sequoias or redwoods would ever die unless destroyed by natural causes such as wind storms, fires or the gradual changing of climates. Slowly, as the years pass, they grow ever larger, adding growth ring to growth ring. Even though lightning often strikes the redwoods it seldom kills them. Observers have seen lightning strike a redwood six times during a single storm. Redwood sap is poisonous to boring insects and rot. The inner, dead wood is well-protected by the living layers of sapwood and by the thick, asbestos-like bark on the outside. Some biologists believe that these trees might easily live for at least 10,000 years.

It will help us to appreciate these venerable trees if we consider what has happened in the world since they sprouted from seeds the size of pinheads so long ago. Some of the Big Tree Sequoias now living had already reached large size when the Egyptian Pharoahs built the Pyramids beside the Nile and when Alexander set out to conquer the known world. When Christ was born the trees were already ancient. They have survived

98

Cross-sections of a pine tree cut at three-foot intervals. Notice that the number of rings decreases up the tree. In order to see all the growth rings, a cross-section must be cut near the base of the tree.

fire and storm and drought, slowly pushing their towering trunks into the California sky. Ancient Greece and the Roman Empire flowered and passed away. The stone structures they built crumbled to ruin. Slowly the pageant of history marched down the pages of time to the present. But the Big Trees grew on, unaffected by the passing centuries. They reach across time, linking the past with the present. In a way, they are also our links with the future because many of them will go on living and growing long after we are gone.

SAVE-THE-REDWOODS LEAGUE

Coastal redwoods in Humboldt County, California

CHAPTER 7

The Big and the Famous

Size alone does not always indicate the age of a tree. A 75-year-old cottonwood may be three feet in diameter, while a California bristlecone pine only three inches in diameter may be 700 years old. Cottonwoods grow rapidly while bristlecone pines grow in situations where life is hard and growth is slow. The Sequoias, as we have already seen, grow to great size and age. Some of the Big Tree Sequoias measure more than 30 feet in diameter and are almost 4,000 years old. On the other hand, one large Sequoia that was cut down measured 27 feet across and was found to be only 1,244 years old. Like most other trees, the sizes of the Sequoias depend on the availability of moisture, as well as other factors. The cutting of the Sequoia mentioned above took place about a hundred years ago and required the labor of five men for 22 days. The stump was so large that as many as sixteen couples once danced cotillions and quadrilles on it. There is an old photograph in existence, taken shortly after the tree was felled, showing 52 men standing around the outer edge of the stump. Other Big Trees that are but little larger are believed to be much older. Naturalist John Muir found one tree in the King's River Forest that measured 35 feet, 8 inches in diameter four feet above the ground. This tree had been burned nearly halfway through, exposing its rings, so that its age could be determined. It was over 4,000 years old. It was Mr. Muir's belief that the ages of some of the Big Trees still standing might be more than 5,000 years. It is impossible, of course, to determine exactly the ages of the largest, living trees. We can only make guesses.

It is easy to imagine the astonishment of the first white men who saw the Sequoias. As far as can be determined the first explorers to see them were members of the Spanish Portolá Expedition in 1769. The facts were recorded by Fray Juan Crespi, who says that they traveled over "low hills, well forested with very high trees of a red color, not known to us." Because of the red color of the wood, they named these trees *palo colorado*, "red tree." Later, Spanish explorers discovered an unusually tall Sequoia and called it *palo alto*, "tall tree." These early travelers probably saw the coastal Sequoias, which are tall but do not have the girth and massive size of the Big Trees found on the high mountains.

Probably the first white men to see the Big Tree Sequoias of the mountains were members of an exploration party under Joseph R. Walker, who traveled overland to California in 1833. The facts were recorded by Zenas Leonard, clerk of the expedition. Naturally, no one believed the "big tree" tales told by early travelers. They were thought to be just more wild tales of the West. It was many years before the actual size of the trees was common knowledge. Probably the largest of the Sequoias is the General Sherman Big Tree in Sequoia National Park, which measures 115 feet in circumference and 272 feet in height. By actual measurement, it contains 600,120 board feet of lumber. Its bark is 24 inches thick. It was named by a hunter and trapper who discovered it in 1879. He had served under General Sherman during the Civil War. The tallest tree is probably the Founder's Tree, a coastal Sequoia, near Dyerville, California, which towers about 364 feet, making it the tallest tree on earth today. This tree, however, is only 47 feet in circumference. One of these forest giants may weigh as much as 3,000,000 pounds—

as much as a small ship. Perhaps the best known of the Big Trees is the Wawona Tree which has a roadway cut through its trunk. The tunnel was cut in 1881 by two Scribner brothers, who labored for a year at the task. The tunnel is 10 feet high, 8 feet wide, and 26 feet long. Apparently, the cutting of this hole has not affected the health of the tree. It continues to grow, regardless of the stream of tourists that each year passes, antlike, through its strange portal. As might be imagined, such large trees need great root systems to hold them erect and to supply them with water and minerals. The root system of a mature Big Tree spreads over two or three acres.

It might be well to straighten out the classification of the California Sequoias. So far, the names redwood, Sequoia and Big Tree have been used rather loosely. Actually, there are *two* different kinds of trees involved. First, there are the coastal redwoods, named *Sequoia sempervirens.* These trees are more slender than their relatives and thrive in the mild, foggy climate of the coast. They are fast growing; a 20-year-old tree may be 8 inches in diameter and 50 feet tall. They range from the southwestern corner of Oregon south to Monterey County, California. Only rarely are they found at higher elevations. They reach the age of about 2,000 years and heights of 350 feet. They are often grown successfully in other areas. The Founder's Tree mentioned above belongs to this group. It was named in honor of the founders of the Save-The-Redwoods League.

The redwoods of the high Sierras have been given a different scientific name by botanists. They are called *Sequoia gigantea.* Usually they are called the Big Trees, a most fitting name since some of them are the world's oldest and largest living things. They may not be as tall as the coastal redwoods, but they are larger in girth. The General Sherman Sequoia is a Big Tree. The Big Trees thrive only in the cold temperatures of the high mountains where snows often blanket the ground to depths of 20 feet. Their range in elevation extends from 5,000 to 8,400 feet above

SAVE-THE-REDWOODS LEAGUE

The Big Tree Sequoias are America's largest trees. This one in California's Calaveras County is several thousand years old.

sea level. The name Sequoia comes from a Cherokee Indian leader named Sequoyah, who invented a Cherokee alphabet, making possible the publication of the New Testament and a newspaper for his people.

SAVE-THE-REDWOODS LEAGUE

*These are coastal redwoods in California. They grow very tall but
do not reach the girth of the Big Trees of the mountains.*

The two kinds of Sequoias are "living fossils," survivors of a
very ancient race that grew in many other parts of the world
millions of years ago. At various periods during geological history their ancestors grew in Greenland, the British Isles, Europe,

105

Asia, Japan and parts of eastern United States. Botanists were quite amazed a few years ago when a small grove of primitive Sequoias was found growing near Chungking, China. These survivors of the ancient Sequoia tribe have been called "dawn redwoods." Huge, fossilized trunks of prehistoric redwoods have been found in many places. You can see specimens in Yellowstone National Park.

The Sequoias are not the only trees that grow to huge size, however. In the State of Oaxaca, Mexico, there is a Montezuma cypress, known as the Tree of Tule, that has a circumference of 117 feet and a height of 141 feet. It stands in the churchyard of Santa Maria del Tule (Holy Mary of the Bulrushes). Its age has been variously estimated all the way from 4,000 to 6,000 years. The Montezuma cypress is a relative of the bald cypress of the United States. These trees are considered to be symbols of mourning and, long ago, their branches were used at funerals.

While no tree in the world can rival the massive sizes of California's Big Trees, the Douglas fir of northwestern United States and Canada often grows to great size. One specimen felled in 1895 in the Lynn Valley, North Vancouver, Canada, was 417 feet tall. This is probably the world's record for tree height. It measured 75 feet around the base and its estimated age was 1,800 years. Recently, a 200-foot Douglas fir in Oregon was blown down by a wind storm. Its trunk was 15.48 feet in diameter and it was 1,000 years old. This was believed to have been the largest fir in Oregon.

There are record trees of various kinds in other places. The Senator, a record cypress in Big Tree Park near Sanford, Florida, is 126 feet tall and has a girth of 42.9 feet. Its age is estimated at between 3,000 and 3,500 years. This is the largest tree east of the Rockies; there is a taller cypress in Arkansas, measuring 180 feet. A loblolly pine near Crossett, Arkansas, is probably the largest of its kind. It is 130 feet tall and 4½ feet in diameter.

Probably no trees in America have as much romance con-

One of the world's largest magnolias grows near the mouth of the Pasca-
goula River in Mississippi where mist often blankets the ground. Its limbs
have a spread of 90 feet and its trunk measures 12.5 feet in circumference.

nected with them as the magnolias. An ancient tribe whose ancestors trace their lineage far back into ancient time, they are
among the oldest of flowering trees as well as the most beautiful.
Each spring, in the South, they spread their great white blooms
for pollination by beetles. Due to the varied shapes of these trees
it is difficult to decide which is the largest. There is one in Washington, Arkansas, that is claimed to hold the record. It has a
trunk circumference of 14 feet and is 65 feet tall. Its spreading
branches cover a circle 65 feet in diameter. There is another
ancient magnolia growing beside the Pascagoula or "Singing
River" in Mississippi, having a crown spread of 90 feet and

107

measuring 12.5 feet in circumference. Its massive moss-covered branches arise low on the short trunk and spread far out. It is not a tall tree, yet one spring the owner counted this tree's blooms and found that there were 9,000.

The sizes of large trees are usually given only in terms of their trunk circumferences or diameters, but this does not take into consideration their spread or height. The American Forestry Association uses the following measurements: The circumference or girth in feet, four-and-one-half feet above the ground, is measured, and to this is added the total height in inches, plus one-quarter of the crown spread in feet. The resulting figure gives a composite picture of the tree. In this way a tall, slender tree can be compared to a low tree having a large trunk.

Trees, like men, have often played important parts in history. In many instances historic events have been enacted beneath their spreading branches. New Orleans has its Dueling Oak (a live oak), beneath which many duels were fought. Hartford, Connecticut, had its Charter Oak, in a cavity of which the charter of the Connecticut Colony was once hidden. This charter had been granted by King Charles II, and served Connecticut as a constitution from 1662 to 1816. No figures are available as to the tree's size, but when it blew down in 1856 a funeral ceremony was held in its honor. It is probably the only tree in history that has been so honored. It was believed to have been a thousand years old.

Certain trees have been associated with many famous people in one way or another. There are a number of trees still living at Mount Vernon that were planted under George Washington's direction. These include tulip poplar, buckeye, elm, pecan, holly, linden, hemlock and mulberry. There is an elm growing near the Senate wing of the United States Capitol under which, it is said, Washington often stood while watching the construction of the Capitol. There are "Washington trees" in many other places that are believed to have been associated, in one way or another,

108

RUTGERS UNIVERSITY

This white oak, formerly standing at New Brunswick, New Jersey, was reputedly the inspiration for Joyce Kilmer's poem "Trees."

with the first president. Other presidents, too, have had a hand in planting various trees. The large elm on the White House grounds was planted by John Quincy Adams. The Grant Elm was planted on the lawn of the Woodstock Academy in Connecticut in 1870. Buffalo Bill is believed to have played, as a small boy, under an elm near Le Claire, Iowa. Naturally, it is known as the Buffalo Bill Elm. Poets and writers have often been immortalized by certain trees, which is probably better than being immortalized in stone. Stone crumbles away, while trees go on living. The Evangeline Oak at St. Martinville, Louisiana, marks the spot where the Acadians landed in 1758, after being driven from Nova Scotia. The story is recounted in Longfellow's poem "Evangeline." Sidney Lanier wrote "The Marshes of Glynn" under the Lanier Oak at Brunswick, Georgia. There was, until 1929, an oak in California known as the Mark Twain

This is the Dueling Oak, an ancient live oak tree growing in New Orleans near the shore of Lake Pontchartrain. At one time numerous duels were fought beneath its branches.

Oak. It is said that Mark Twain wrote "The Celebrated Jumping Frog of Calaveras County," the yarn that give him his first fame, in its shade.

In Athens, Georgia, there once grew an oak that testified to the love of one man for a tree. Its owner, William H. Jackson, willed to the oak, itself and possession of all land within 8 feet. The deed, duly recorded by the town clerk, is dated 1820. Since most trees live far longer than men, they have often been used as boundary markers. Such trees are called "witness trees" and are still recognized by courts of law in land disputes.

As an indication of people's admiration and love of trees, each state has formally adopted its favorite tree as the State Tree. They are as follows:

Alabama — Slash pine
Alaska — Sitka spruce
Arizona — Honey mesquite
Arkansas — Shortleaf pine
California — Redwood
Colorado — Blue spruce
Connecticut — White oak
Delaware — American holly
Florida — Cabbage palmetto
Georgia — Longleaf pine
Hawaii — Kukui (candlenut)
Idaho — Western pine
Illinois — Bur oak
Indiana — Tulip poplar
Iowa — Black walnut
Kansas — Cottonwood
Kentucky — Tulip poplar
Louisiana — Magnolia
Maine — Pine
Maryland — White oak
Massachusetts — American elm
Michigan — Apple
Minnesota — Norway pine
Mississippi — Magnolia
Missouri — Hawthorn

Montana — Ponderosa pine
Nebraska — Cottonwood
Nevada — Pinyon pine
New Hampshire — Yellow birch
New Jersey — Atlantic white cedar
New Mexico — Pinyon pine
New York — Maple
North Carolina — Dogwood
North Dakota — Green ash
Ohio — Buckeye
Oklahoma — Redbud
Oregon — Douglas fir
Pennsylvania — Eastern hemlock
Rhode Island — Maple
South Carolina — Cabbage palmetto
South Dakota — Cottonwood
Tennessee — Red cedar
Texas — Pecan
Utah — Blue spruce
Vermont — Sugar maple
Virginia — Dogwood
Washington — Western hemlock
West Virginia — White oak
Wisconsin — Sugar maple
Wyoming — Lodge pole pine

Many of the world's large or famous trees grow in foreign lands. England has many famous trees. The oaks have been revered there since the days of the ancient Druids. It was under the Parliament Oak, for example, that Parliament assembled in 1695. It was under the Arkenwyke Yew at Runnymede that the Magna Charta was signed.

Dr. Ferdinand Lane saw an ancient olive tree in the vicinity of Jerusalem that was supposed to have been standing when Jesus visited the spot. Strange indeed is the dragon tree that grows in Africa and other places. The largest dragon tree on record grew, until 1867, on Teneriffe, one of the Canary Islands. It was only 70 feet tall but had a girth of 79 feet. It is believed to have been about 6,000 years old. These trees belong to the botanical genus *Dracaena* and are called dragon trees or dragon's blood trees because of their red sap, which has been used in medicine and as a coloring agent in varnish.

According to Dr. Lane, it is probable that the tree having the greatest girth in the world is a European chestnut growing in Sicily. It is now badly mutilated, but its girth is stated by various authorities as being between 174 and 204 feet! It is known as the Tree of a Hundred Horses because of a legend that Joanna, Spanish Queen of Aragon, and her party of a hundred sought refuge under its branches during a thunderstorm. Its age is unknown.

Among the world's most unusual trees is the baobab, a native of Africa and Australia. Its trunk is more or less jug-shaped and filled with pith for the storage of water. These trees do not grow to great height, usually not over 45 feet tall, but the girth of a large specimen may be 90 feet. Natives use the hollowed-out trunks of these strange trees as dwellings and also fashion dugout canoes from small specimens. There are some other trees found in various parts of the world that have their trunks enlarged into bottle-like shapes for water or food storage. One is the barriguda or "big bellied" tree of Brazil. Another is the bottle

The banyan starts life as an epiphyte growing on the side of a tree. Eventually the "host" tree is destroyed and the banyan, a type of strangler fig, grows to great size. This specimen in Florida is 135 feet in diameter. Note the numerous supporting prop roots extending down from the limbs.

palm of Cuba and the nearby Isle of Pines. It is called the "pot belly" tree, and the trunks are sometimes used as watering troughs and beehives.

Another strange tree is the banyan that starts its life as a vine growing on another tree. In tropical countries I have seen banyans that covered large areas. One can crawl far back into the dark interior of the trees by squeezing between the many trunks or aerial prop-roots. In some places, natives believe that evil spirits dwell inside the trees. Since hornets and snakes often make these trees their abodes, such beliefs are quite understandable. Because of its strange mode of growth, it is impossible to compare the size of this tree with others of more conventional form. The fact remains that they often grow very large. Truly, the world's trees grow in many shapes and sizes; each is fitted for the life it lives.

Each tree produces wood having special characteristics. Here are six cross-sections of common trees. Beginning at the left, the samples are as follows. Top row: birch, cedar, sycamore. Middle row: bois d'arc, willow, pine. Bottom row: sweet gum, catalpa, sassafras.

CHAPTER 8

Of Woods and Men

Somewhere, long ago in some forgotten cave, man first warmed his hands before a fire he had made himself. He had gathered fagots from the surrounding forest and obtained a glowing ember, probably from a lightning-struck tree. Some other ancient man found black "rocks" that would burn with great heat. He had discovered coal, but both coal from the earth and fagots from the forest were really the same thing. Each contained stored heat from the sun, and each was a product of trees. The coal contained heat from the sun that, a million years previously, had shed its rays upon a forest.

Certainly, when we take into consideration all the things that trees and their products have done for us, we soon realize that without them our lives would be far different. Ever since the human race began, men have depended upon trees for many necessities. Even the Eskimos, dwelling hundreds of miles north of the last living trees, fashion sleighs from driftwood gathered from the beaches. It was from trees that men made their earliest weapons, first the spear, then the bow and arrow. For thousands of years men defended themselves with the wooden bow and arrow, and although it is now used mainly for sport, more men have been slain in battle with the bow and arrow than with either gun powder or atomic bombs. The black powder used in muzzle-loading guns was composed of wood charcoal, sulphur and saltpeter, however.

Primitive man eventually learned to build shelters from wood and no longer depended upon caves or skin tents. Most of us still live in wooden houses; only the methods of constructing them have changed. Wood is still the most practical and versatile of building materials. As languages developed, men found that their thoughts could be recorded for others to read. At first this was done on stone and clay tablets; then came the invention of paper, made from wood pulp, an almost perfect medium upon which to write or print. Wood is being used more and more for almost every conceivable purpose. Someday, perhaps, our supplies of coal, iron and petroleum will be used up, but, if we use our forest products wisely, we will still have wood. This is because trees continue to grow. Unfortunately, at the present time mankind is using about 50 billion cubic feet of wood a year but it is estimated that only about 40 billion cubic feet of new wood is being grown. The world may eventually be faced with a serious wood shortage if effective conservation practices are not followed.

Down the ages trees have furnished the materials from which man built his canoes and ships. At first he used log rafts to cross or float down rivers, then he constructed dugouts by laboriously hollowing out logs and shaping them to canoe-like form. Not only did early men navigate wide rivers in these dugouts but successfully crossed great oceans. In some cases outriggers were added to give these sea-going dugouts more stability, and such boats are still used in many parts of the world. The American Indians stripped the bark from birch trees and fashioned it into canoes that were both light and strong. The seams were made watertight with tree rosin.

Later, men built great wooden ships and the age of commerce and world exploration began. It is only in recent years that people have gone down to the sea in anything except wooden ships. The art of ship building is an ancient craft. Several thousand years ago it came into flower in eastern Mediterranean lands and spread on to Rome and England. The great oak forests of England furnished the wood for her naval and merchant ships which plied every sea and made her, at last, a great world power. In wooden ships Columbus discovered the New World and the Pilgrims braved the Atlantic. World geography was changed and the course of human history expanded across new horizons. There was no ocean too wide or too stormy but some adventurous souls dared cross it in their fragile wooden vessels. No chapter in history is more filled with both romance and violence than the days when pirate ships roamed the Spanish Main. It was truly a time of "wooden ships and iron men."

Peoples in other lands than the Old World were also busy constructing sea-going vessels. It is believed by some scientists that the South Pacific islands were settled long ago by natives of South America who crossed the vast South Pacific in balsa rafts. It was to prove that this could be done that Thor Heyerdahl and his crew navigated their fragile balsa raft, *Kon-Tiki*, across the Pacific from Peru to Tahiti.

In many tropical lands natives construct dugout canoes by hollowing out large logs. In such canoes they cross lakes, rivers and even seas.

The present age has been called the Age of Plastics, yet many plastics are made from wood. Dry wood is about 99 per cent cellulose, a material that can be made into many products, including rayon, celluloid and photographic film. Even human food may someday be made from wood. Chemists have already learned how to break cellulose down into sugar. Starch and sugar are carbohydrates containing carbon, hydrogen and oxygen, and cellulose is quite similar to starch in chemical composition. Wood cellulose is now being broken down into wood molasses and used as stock feed. A ton of dry wood will yield 180 gallons of molasses. Thus, it is easily possible that we may eventually turn to the forests for at least some of our food.

In addition to investigating wood as possible sources of foods, chemists have been busy in other respects. They have been able to break wood fibers down and compress them into hard composition board that is far superior to the original wood. They have also sliced wood into thin sheets and cemented them together with special glues. The result is laminated wood, some kinds of which are stronger than steel.

In addition to cellulose, an important constituent of wood is a hard substance called lignin. It is found in the cell walls and gives wood much of its strength. Hard woods such as oak and walnut contain more lignin than soft woods such as poplar and pine. Many tropical woods like lignum-vitae have a high lignin content and are, thus, very hard and heavy. The wood of many tropical trees will not float in water. Most books give the weights of various woods in terms of their *specific gravities*. These are calculated as their weights relative to that of water, which weighs 62.4 pounds per cubic foot. As an example, wood which weighs 31.2 pounds per cubic foot (one-half that of water) is said to have a specific gravity of 0.5. Since this wood is lighter than water it will float. Wood such as ironwood weighs 80 pounds per cubic foot and, since it is much heavier than water, it will sink. Ironwood has a specific gravity of 1.28. Let us com-

118

pare the actual weights of various kinds of woods in terms of
their weights per cubic foot.

KIND OF WOOD	POUNDS PER CU. FT.
Lighter than water — floats:	
Aeschynomene (Cuba)	3
Balsa (Central America)	6 to 25
Corkwood (Florida)	13
Ceibo (Argentina)	15
White pine (U. S.)	22
Quaking aspen (U. S.)	25
Longleaf pine (U. S.)	31
Birch (U. S.)	44
Sugar maple (U. S.)	44
Beech (U. S.)	45
White oak (U. S.)	47
Black locust (U. S.)	48
Persimmon (U. S.)	49
Osage orange (U. S.)	50
Hickory (U. S.)	51
Heavier than water — sinks:	
Poison ash (Mexico)	69
Ebony (West Indies)	77
Ironwood (S. America)	80
Leadwood (Florida)	81
Letterwood (S. America)	83
Lignum-vitae (Tropics)	87
Black ironwood (Florida and Tropics)	93

From the above table it is seen that Florida corkwood is probably the lightest wood native to North America. These trees
range from Florida, north to Georgia and west to Texas. They
thrive in swamps and swamp borders. The wood is sometimes
used for fish net floats. (Commercial cork at 15 pounds per cubic
foot weighs more than Florida corkwood.) Our heaviest native
wood is Florida leadwood, a native of southern Florida and the
West Indies. It grows in hammocks near tide water. The wood
apparently has no commercial value.

Various woods have different densities or weights. Here are shown one-inch cubes of four different woods in water. Balsa, at left, is lightest. The next lightest is pine, followed by black walnut, oak, and ironwood, which sinks because it is heavier than water.

The world's lightest woods are the balsas, of which there are half a dozen kinds. Balsa trees grow in Central and South America where large specimens often attain heights of 90 feet. They are fast growing; a two-year-old tree may measure 30 feet. During World War II balsa wood was considered to be a strategic material since it was used for mine floats. A mine barrier across the North Sea, 250 miles long, was supported by balsa logs. Trees of the genus *Aeschynomene* occur in many parts of the world but mostly in tropical areas, although some kinds are also found in our own Southeast. In South America the feather-weight pith is used for corks and for stropping razors. In the Orient, it is used in pith helmets, fish net floats, and for making artificial flowers.

One of the most useful trees of all is the coconut palm. The trunk of a palm is different from that of most other trees. There

120

is no cambium, no growth rings and no heartwood. There are no branches, either. Actually, the trunk of a palm is more like a stalk of corn than a tree. It is spongy and with many hard fibers, yet it is very strong. It is supple enough to bend in winds that would snap off a pine. The wood itself is not important in commerce, but when seasoned it becomes very hard, and a number of things can be made out of it.

Foresters divide woods into two groups. First there are the *softwoods* represented by pine, spruce, fir, cypress, redwood and yew. Most of these trees have needle-like leaves and are called evergreens. Then there are the *hardwoods* such as hickory, oak, maple, elm, cottonwood, walnut and mahogany. Some of the woods so classified do not always fit in their categories, however. Southern pine, for example, is harder than many so-called hardwoods. Cottonwood, classified as "hardwood," is quite soft.

Some woods last a long while, even when cut down and made into furniture and other useful things. Consider the fact that the solid heartwood of a redwood may be several thousand years old. Scientists have recently discovered that redwood contains

Samples of four different kinds of wood. This is the standard method of exhibiting wood samples.

SASSAFRAS   BOIS D'ARC   BIRCH   SYCAMORE

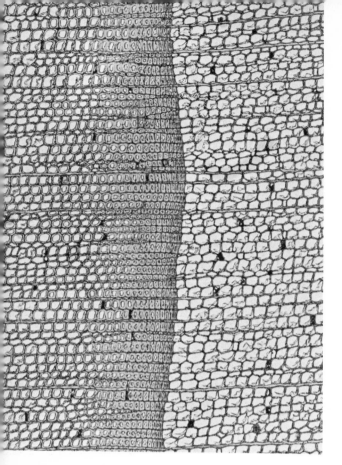

A microscopic view of pine xylem. At right is the spring-wood; at center is darker summerwood with its thick cell walls. The sharp division at the center is where growth ceased in winter.

a substance they have named "sempervirin," after the scientific name of the tree, which prevents the wood from decaying. Chemically, this material is closely related to carbolic acid, which is, itself, an excellent wood preservative. Redwood, like cypress and teak, is also resistant to termite and other insect attack.

The strengths of various woods often determine the uses to which they can be put. In the case of softwoods, growth is very rapid in spring, the time when the soft, porous portion of the annual growth ring is being produced. During summer, a layer of hard summerwood is produced. The more summerwood produced, the harder and stronger the lumber. A high proportion of summerwood also means greater weight.

The strengths of hardwoods depend largely on the presence of many thick-walled pores in the summerwood. During growth,

122

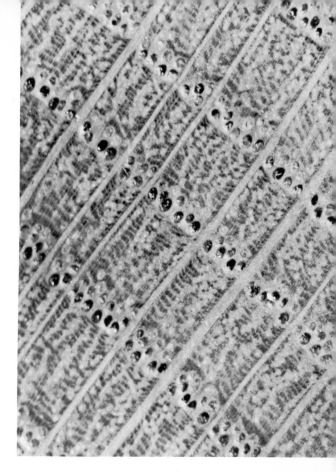

A microscopic view of oak wood. Zones containing pores were produced in spring during rapid growth. The summerwood zones are dense and heavy. Here, growth is toward the upper right.

these pores carry liquids of various kinds. In hardwoods such as oak, elm, and ash, the springwood pores are larger than those in summerwood. These trees are called "ring-porous" woods. In other hardwoods the spring and summerwood rings are the same size. Examples are maple, gum, magnolia and birch. The presence or absence of these large pores may determine the use of the wood. Barrels cannot be made of red oak, which has large pores, because liquids would leak out. For such a purpose, white oak is used because the pores become clogged during growth.

Thick-walled fibers that spiral up through the tissues of hardwood trees also add to their strength. Sometimes these fibers spiral one way and sometimes the other. The pretty grain of some woods like maple and mahogany is the result of these spiral fibers. Veneers, or thin sheets, cut from such woods are often marked with patterns described as "curly," "quilted," "fiddle-

123

back" or "bird's-eye." These are called "figured" woods. Stradivarius, the master violin maker, used curly-grained fir for the bellies of his violins, while pear, beech or other hardwood was used for the backs of his violins. Most modern furniture is finished with thin layers of veneer glued to the outside surfaces. This veneer is obtained by rotating a log held in a lathelike machine while a long, sharp blade is held against it. The veneer rolls off the log as a paper-thin sheet. Many of the most beautiful veneers are obtained in this manner from both native and tropical woods.

As a tree grows it is influenced by many things. Sometimes high winds bend trees over. Such trees may straighten up, but if they are later sawed in two it will be found that the growth rings on the lower side are very wide. This is called "compression" wood. The formation of this compression wood also occurs normally on the undersides of pine limbs. It is a natural result of the weight of the limb, and can be easily seen when limbs are sawed off. In the case of hardwoods, this thickening of the growth rings occurs on the *upper* sides of the limbs. This is

A cypress "knee" sawed in half to show how the porous, air-conducting wood looks. These "knees" arise from the roots.

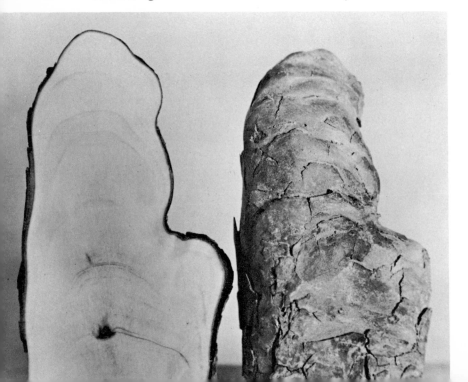

In a cross-section of a pine limb, the growth rings on the lower side are thickened. This is called compression wood *and results from the unequal strains on the upper and lower parts of the limb. In oaks, compression wood is located on the upper sides of the limbs.*

called *tension* wood. Both compression and tension woods are of poor quality for construction.

When one considers the great wind pressure that large trees must resist, it is remarkable that they can remain standing at all. In addition, the great weight of the tree must be supported. Nature has designed the tree in such a way that it is not only held upright but is able to resist high winds. In large pines and hardwoods the inner wood bears the weight of the tree while the outer layers pull from all sides, holding it erect. Foresters have found that each square inch of center wood may support as much as 1,500 pounds of weight.

Sometimes trees with strangely twisted trunks are seen. They are often encountered at high mountain elevations where the spiral grain is most easily seen in dead trees from which the bark has fallen away. Such trees may twist to either the right or the left but, apparently, most trees are "right handed"; that is, their grain spirals to the right. A forester in the State of Washington observed 400 twisted trees and found that 96 per cent had right-handed spirals. It was also found that 85 per cent of the firs in Colorado spiraled to the right. By contrast, only 25 per cent of the Douglas firs in the coastal area of Washington were right-handed. Tree spirals may be either short or long. In the case of mountain junipers, the grain may make a complete spiral every two feet!

This brings up the old question of vine spirals. Some people believe that vines spiral one way in the Northern Hemisphere and the opposite way in the Southern Hemisphere. This reasoning is based on the fact that, due to the earth's rotation, hurricanes rotate to the left north of the Equator and to the right south of the Equator. The truth is that some vines spiral up trees in one direction and some in the other. Vines like the hop may spiral either way. The same reasoning has been applied to the spirals of tree grain, but most authorities do not believe there is any connection. Corkscrew trees are apparently the results of environment and of an inherited tendency to twist. We might note here that, in a certain section of Panama, some trees tend to grow *square*. The same kinds of trees growing in other places are of the usual form. This is a mystery that needs more study.

The fine woods used in furniture often come from distant lands. Rosewood, with its beautiful grain and roselike smell, comes from Brazil, Jamaica and Honduras. Mahogany, of which there are several kinds, is cut and loaded on ships in Rhodesia, the Philippines and Central and South America. Ebony, a close

As trees grow old, their limbs often become gnarled and twisted. This ancient post oak is covered with mosses and ferns.

relative of our native persimmon, comes all the way from Africa, India and Ceylon. From the deep forests of Burma comes teak, considered the queen of woods. It is harvested with the aid of trained elephants. Aromatic sandalwood is cut on the islands of the East Indies and in India. From tropical America comes coco-bolo wood from Dalbergia trees. It must be worked with care because the wood is poisonous, although not after being finished. To our cabinet makers and makers of fine furniture also come striped zebrawood from the jungles of tropical America and ipil from the Philippines. Fine woods are romantic products and, like spices and perfumes, often come to us from the world's far places.

127

Almost every part of the coconut palm is put to use.

CHAPTER 9

The Things They Make

The valuable woods produced by trees are of great importance
to us, yet trees are also the sources of many other useful things.
When entering a thatched hut in the Tropics I was always surprised at its coolness. The thick thatch of palm leaves or fronds
is an excellent insulation against the sun's heat, even at mid-day.
In addition to thatching material, palm leaves are woven into
baskets of many shapes and sizes. I once came upon a native in
a jungle valley weaving a large number of small baskets. When
asked what they were for, he told me they were hens' nests! To
many of the world's people the coconut tree is the staff of life,
and many tropical islands would be uninhabitable were it not for
this tree. Almost every part of it has some use. The fruit or nut
is opened and the meat is eaten raw or cooked. From the meat
also is extracted oil used for cooking and soap making. At the
end of the coconut are three round scars, making it look like a
monkey's face. Just inside the largest scar lies the embryo. When
the coconut sprouts, the young leaves emerge at this point. It is
not unusual to see large numbers of fallen coconuts lying on the
ground with clusters of leaves growing from them. It is in this
way that new coconut trees come into being. If a hole is punched
through this large scar, the "milk," which makes a refreshing
drink, can be drained out. Coconut milk is also used in cooking
taro and other foods.

A coconut tree may live from 60 to 70 years and produce about a hundred nuts a year. After the nuts are gathered the surrounding husk is removed by striking them on a sharpened stake driven in the ground. The shell is then broken open and the meat removed and dried. This dried coconut meat is called copra and contains from 50 to 70 per cent oil. The United States imports about 20 million pounds a year. The residue remaining after the oil is extracted is called coco cake and makes excellent stock feed. The stiff, elastic fiber from the husk, known as *coir*, is also useful for bagging, matting, door mats, brushes and ropes. In contact with sea water it is superior to hemp. From the hard shell of the nut, natives make various containers, such as cups and bowls. When used as a fuel the shells produce a hot flame.

From the terminal bud of the coconut palm is obtained a delicacy called palm cabbage, and the inner parts of young stems are also eaten. The stems which hold the developing clusters of nuts are sometimes cut off and the juice which flows from them collected in buckets. This juice is either made into a fermented beverage called *tuba-tuba* or boiled down to make a sugar called *jaggery*. In some places the natives even make use

The fronds of the nipa palm arise from the stem, which grows beneath the mud along tropical streams. It is much used for thatching native huts.

Coconut husks are used in making mats, ropes and brushes. The meat is eaten or dried into copra for its valuable oil. The milk is a refreshing drink.

of the roots from which they obtain a narcotic. In the United States, coconut palms grow in southern Florida and California, although not as a commercial crop.

Many other palms are valuable to us. One kind is the date palm which often grows to heights of 100 feet and produces 300 to 400 pounds of nutritious fruit. Date palms, native to Arabia and North Africa, are grown in Arizona and California. Another important member of this family is the sago palm which stores large quantities of pure starch in its trunk.

From the standpoint of human food, our own sugar maple trees that grow in many parts of northeastern United States are an important source. Sugars of various kinds are produced by all trees, being the direct result of photosynthesis in green leaves. Most of this tree sugar is in the form of *glucose* or *fructose*, but the sugar maple trees manufacture ordinary cane sugar or *sucrose*. It was harvested by the Indians long before the white man came. Vermont leads in maple sugar production. At the approach of "sap weather" the owners of sugar groves begin preparation for the harvest which comes in late winter, a time of mild days and freezing nights, although snow still covers the ground. Spouts are inserted in the bark and the syrup allowed to drip into buckets. With more modern methods, the spouts are all connected together with plastic tubing and the sap flows into a container at one central collecting station. After collection the syrup or sap is boiled down and refined; the result is delicious maple sugar. Other trees in other parts of the world also yield sugar—the toddy palm of Burma, the carob tree of Mediterranean countries, the mesquite tree of our Southwest and the tamarisk of the Near East. Coconut palm jaggery has already been mentioned.

When the bark of pines in our Southeast is tapped, turpentine is obtained, and when rubber trees are tapped, rubber or latex flows out. Other trees that yield substances from slits in their bark are the massaranduba tree of Malaya from which is obtained "gutta-percha," which is similar to rubber but more durable. One of the most interesting products bled from trees is chicle. This is the chief constituent of chewing gum. It is obtained from the sapodilla tree of Central America through slanting gashes made in the bark. Sapodilla trees are never abundant, but grow scattered through the jungle. Incidentally, lumber sawed from these trees is very hard, durable and takes a high polish. It was used in ancient Mayan temples.

There are numerous trees that yield milky juices when their bark is pierced. If a knife is drawn across the trunk of a breadfruit tree, a white latex oozes out. This latex is very sticky but does not harden. In my first experience with breadfruit latex, I

132

thought I had discovered a new kind of rubber. I made all sorts of experiments with it in the laboratory, but the result was nothing more than a sticky mess. Natives in tropical countries where breadfruit trees grow use this latex for capturing small birds. It is smeared on tree limbs, where birds alight and become entangled. As a matter of fact, the famous and valuable feather cloaks worn by Hawaiian kings were made from the plumage of birds captured in this way. True rubber is obtained from a tree native to the Amazon jungle. Its scientific name is *Hevea brasiliensis*. From the tree's standpoint, the latex which oozes out of its bark forms a natural protection against injury. Breaks in the bark are sealed with the insoluble latex. In harvesting the latex, a workman cuts a diagonal strip of bark from one side of the tree and the latex which oozes out is caught in cups. Upon exposure to air it hardens into crude rubber.

In South America, before the coming of the white man, this rubber was collected by natives and used for various purposes such as making rubber balls. On his second voyage to the New World, Columbus saw Indians playing a game with a ball of crude rubber, a strange, new substance to the Spaniards. The saga of rubber began when its many industrial applications were discovered. Great rubber plantations in the Amazon region came into existence and wealth flowed into the areas where rubber trees could be grown. The city of Manáos on the Rio Negro, a tributary of the Amazon, became the center of the rubber empire. It was called the "Paris of the Jungle" and at one time had an opera house costing millions of dollars. In time, rubber trees were taken to Malaya and Sumatra where they flourished and where rubber could be produced more economically. As a result, the South American rubber boom burst and Manáos is now a sleepy city. The opera house is still there, a reminder of the glory that came for a brief time to this remote city in the jungle.

Travelers in the coastal areas of Florida, Alabama, Georgia, and Mississippi are apt to see longleaf and slash pines that are

Rubber trees are bled for their latex rubbers, useful in industry. At one time this natural rubber was the only source of material for automobile tires.

being "turpentined." The trunks of such trees have "faces" from which the bark has been cut away, a little at a time, until the "face" is several feet high. At the lower edge is attached a metal trough in which the pitch is collected, much as latex rubber is collected. About once a week a special tool is used to make another diagonal cut at the upper edge of the "face" to keep the pitch flowing. Periodically, the metal collecting troughs are emptied and the pitch taken to the still where it is distilled into liquid turpentine and solidified rosin. These products are used by industry in numerous ways. In the days of wooden ships, pitch and rosin were of vital importance in keeping them watertight. That is the reason that turpentine and rosin are called "naval

Pine trees are "turpentined" to obtain resin. Cuts or "faces" are made in the trunks, and the rosin which runs out is collected in troughs.

stores." Rosins of various kinds have long been used in calking ships. You will recall that the Lord commanded Noah to make the Ark seaworthy by "pitching it within and without with pitch." Honeybees also collect rosin from trees and use it to waterproof their hives. It is called "bee glue" or *propolis.*

In addition to the method of "turpentining" trees described above, turpentine and rosin are obtained by placing old stumps of longleaf and slash pines in special stills and extracting the naval stores. Only the heartwood of old stumps is used. Each year, more than 12 million gallons of turpentine and 50 million pounds of rosin are distilled in this manner.

One of the oldest methods of obtaining various products from

Tung oil used in paints and varnishes is extracted from nuts of the tung oil tree.

wood is that of destructive distillation. In this case the wood is heated and the volatile substances are condensed and collected as in an alcohol still. Many valuable things are obtained, including wood alcohol, acetone, turpentine, tars and acetic acid.

From trees also are obtained various useful oils, waxes and gums. Our paint and varnish industry uses large quantities of tung oil or China wood oil obtained from the walnut-size nuts of tung trees. Formerly, these spreading trees with their attractive flower clusters were grown only in China. Recently, extensive plantings of tung trees have been established in the coastal areas of our southeastern states. Within the shell of the nut are contained from three to seven seeds from which the oil is extracted. These nuts are poisonous and cattle have been killed by eating them. In a few instances, also, people have been made ill by chewing the nuts.

While most of the wax used by industry is the product of honeybees, there are several trees that also yield waxes. Wax myrtle found along our east coast has its berries coated with wax which can be removed and used in making aromatic candles. From the leaves of the wax palm (Copernicia) in Brazil is obtained carnauba wax. It is yellowish and brittle and used in the manufacture of floor polishes, phonograph records and shoe polish. The root of the wax palm is edible.

Useful gums of many sorts have been gathered from trees for many centuries. These include frankincense, asafoetida, myrrh, labdanum, copal, amber and gum arabic. The latter is obtained from *Acacia* trees in Africa and is commonly used in making adhesives, candy and in medicine.

Trees give us many useful things, but none so endowed with romance as the spices which have sometimes been sold for their weights in gold. In search of spices men have braved the sea on voyages to far lands. It was in search of a short route to the Orient and the Spice Islands that Columbus crossed the unknown Atlantic. Not all spices are obtained from trees, but many are. From the Banda Isles comes nutmeg, harvested from the nutmeg tree (*Myristica fragrans*). The East Indies is the source of clove from clove trees, allspice from the berries of the pimenta tree and cinnamon from the aromatic bark of the *Cinnamomum* tree. The fragrance of islands where spice trees grow abundantly can often be smelled far at sea. Is it any wonder they are called Spice Islands?

From trees we also obtain medicines and medicinal products. Some of these have interesting histories. Nearly three hundred years ago, the Spanish Countess of Chinchon became ill from a

The African oil palm yields oil used in making candles, soap, margarine, cooking oil and medical ointments.

tropical disease while in Peru. A medicine made from the bark of a common Peruvian tree was administered and she soon recovered. The disease was malaria, that we now know to be transmitted by the *Anopheles* mosquito. When the Countess returned to Spain she took some of the strange bark with her. The bark contains quinine, a drug that is very effective in the treatment of malaria. In fact, for hundreds of years this bark was the only effective treatment known. The tree, itself, was named cinchona in honor of the Countess of Chinchon.

From the seeds of the *Strychnos* tree of Ceylon, India and Cochin China is obtained strychnine, a powerful poison, but useful in medicine. From the coca tree of the Andes Mountains is obtained cocaine. One of the most interesting drugs is *curare*, obtained from the curare tree of Brazil. For centuries it was used by headhunters for poisoning their blowgun darts. Merely scratching the skin with one of these poisoned darts was enough to cause insensibility. In the language of the Indians *curare* means "poison." Other poisonous trees include the manchineel tree that grows in Central America but is also found on the Florida Keys. It contains a milky juice that irritates the skin. A person's skin may be blistered merely by standing under a manchineel tree in the rain. Other poisonous trees are poison sumacs, Australian stinging trees, and our native buckeye. The berries of the common chinaberry of our Southeast contain a narcotic drug which often stupefies birds which feed upon them.

Our most important vegetable fiber, that from which cotton cloth is spun, comes from cotton plants grown in southern United States and other places. But there is also a wild cotton in the form of small trees that grow in several tropical countries as well as in southern Florida. There is also a tropical tree that produces a fiber used in stuffing cushions and life preservers. This is the ceiba or silk-cotton tree which bears pods several inches long. These pods contain seeds to which the silky fiber is attached, and the fiber is called kapok. Silk-cotton trees tower

138

above other jungle trees, and their branches extend straight out from the sides in a very characteristic manner. From the base of the trunk great wall-like buttresses flare away for many yards. In large trees these may be several feet high.

As if trees had not already done enough for us, they also furnish some of our favorite beverages. It is believed that the native home of the coffee tree (*Coffea arabica*) is Abyssinia, in the province of Kaffa. Wild coffee trees still grow there. The coffee tree belongs to the Madder family and, like most other useful trees, it has been transplanted to many warm parts of the world far from its native mountains. Most of our coffee comes, at present, from Brazil. The fruit of the coffee tree is cherry-like, each one containing two seeds. These are the coffee beans. After harvesting, the beans are cleaned and roasted to bring out their flavor and aroma. Besides the pleasant taste of coffee, it also contains a drug called *caffeine,* which acts as a mild stimulant to the nervous system. In addition to coffee, the wood of the tree is of value since it is hard, heavy and takes a high polish.

Tea, also, is a tree product. In this case, it is the leaves which are used. The tree (*Thea sinensis*) is a close relative to the camellia and is of Chinese origin. Tea has been used as a beverage in China for thousands of years. Our tea comes from Ceylon, India, China and Japan. The leaves are picked by hand while still green and then dried. Like coffee, tea contains caffeine. In the days of the clipper ships sailing out of Salem and Boston, cargoes from the Far East consisted chiefly of tea and silk.

To the chocolate tree we are indebted for chocolate used as a drink and in making candy and pastry. Chocolate trees were originally found growing in Mexico and Central America, and a drink made of chocolate was a favorite with the Aztec Indians long before the white man came to the New World. The first chocolate shop was opened in London in 1657 and chocolate soon became a fashionable drink. The tree grows to heights of about 30 feet and, like many tropical trees, the blooms arise

Coffee beans and the cotton-like fibers of kapok are both useful tree products. At left, a coffee berry containing beans. At right, a kapok pod.

directly from the trunk. The pods, which develop from the blooms, are filled with pink pulp within which are concealed the chocolate beans.

A favorite drink of our South American neighbors is maté, a drink brewed from the leaves of *yerba maté*, a close relative of our native holly. Maté is usually sipped from a gourd through a long tube called a *bombilla*. Like tea and coffee, maté contains caffeine.

Certainly, we should not leave the subject of tree products without mention of their edible fruits. These range from apples to oranges and from pawpaw to breadfruit. The word "apple" was once applied to any kind of fruit. Thus, we have pineapple, oak apple, custard apple and so on. Since ancient times humans have depended upon various tree fruits for part of their food. The fruit trees we are now familiar with—apple, pear, cherry, plum, peach, orange, fig—are much improved over the wild types, however. These new varieties have been developed by plant breeders. Those of us who dwell in temperate climates are not so familiar with the many tropical fruits. Still, to a large percentage of the world's population, such exotic fruits as bread-fruit, carambola, papaya and mango are as commonplace as apples are to us. On many tropical islands the breadfruit is al-most as important as the coconut. The breadfruit tree itself grows to considerable size and its large leaves are many-lobed. It is an attractive tree, the fruit somewhat resembling that of our Osage orange or bois d'arc except that it is more elongate. The pulpy fruit is said to taste like bread, but in my experience I never found this so. The natives of many islands roast or bake the fruit. The tree is native to the Pacific Islands and originally did not grow in the West Indies. The ill-fated voyage of Captain Wil-liam Bligh in the *Bounty* was to obtain breadfruit trees in Tahiti for transplanting in the West Indies as a source of food. The ship's crew mutinied in the Pacific, set Captain Bligh adrift in a small boat, and then sailed the *Bounty* to remote Pitcairn Is-land where they took up life. Their descendants still dwell there. Later, Captain Bligh made a second voyage and was successful in transporting over a thousand young breadfruit trees to the West Indies. Unfortunately, the fruit never became as popular as it had been hoped, but the story of Captain Bligh and the mutiny on the *Bounty* is one of the great sagas of the sea.

In many tropical lands the fruit of the breadfruit tree is an important item of diet. The pulpy fruit is baked or roasted and is said to taste like bread.

Within the leafy expanse of this great live oak live many animals as well as other plants. It is like a teeming city where birds, insects, vines and lichens make their homes.

CHAPTER 10

The World of the Tree

$\mathcal{E}$ach tree in the forest is a small world or *microcosm* within which live many animals and even other plants. It is like a small city with many inhabitants, each with its own problems of obtaining food, mates and nesting sites. The home ranges of these animals vary greatly in size. To an aphid, sucking juices from a leaf, the leaf is its world where it will spend its entire life. Other animals travel from one part of the tree city to another, or to other trees. Some birds, like the jays and mockingbirds, may live out their entire lives within the boundaries of a small woodland, but other birds need more room. Some birds nest in trees in the United States and then migrate thousands of miles away to spend the winter in the Southern Hemisphere. When spring returns to the North, these same individuals fly back, often nesting in the same trees.

Trees are the traditional homes of birds, and most kinds are specialists in their choice of habitats and the kinds of trees they live in. Those that inhabit the vicinities of lakes and ponds are seldom found in other places. The same is true of those that dwell on prairies or in woodlands. Some woodland species live along the margins of forests, rarely venturing far inside. Others prefer the larger trees deeper in the forest. "Perching birds" such as sparrows, wrens and warblers are mostly the birds of the woodland and forests, but there are even differences in the kinds of birds found in upland and lowland forests. Whip-poor-wills, for instance, prefer the dry uplands, while Carolina wrens, the veeries and many warblers are partial to the damper lowland woods.

Birds and other creatures also have preferred portions of trees they inhabit. Some live in the upper story far above the ground; others live in the security of the middle story where they are hidden in the dense foliage. Still others live upon the lower branches or the trunk. Other kinds of animals dwell in the darkness of the tree's underground "basement" or root system.

The middle and upper stories have many tenants. Here gall wasps lay their minute eggs in the leaves and, at the same time, inject some unknown growth stimulant which causes the leaves to create specially made homes for the gall wasps' young. Leaf-eating caterpillars of endless kinds destroy leaves. These range in size from six-inch hickory horned devils, which are huge and fearsome-looking but perfectly harmless, to minute kinds such as leaf miners, so small that they can tunnel between the upper and lower surfaces of the leaves. Other leaf-eating caterpillars are those of the luna, cecropia and polyphemus moths. All these are fed upon by birds, even though they are camouflaged by

Walking-stick insects feed upon the leaves of trees. Their slender forms resemble twigs and camouflage them from their enemies.

Lichens often grow on limbs and trunks of trees. These strange plants are composed of two lowly forms of plant life: a green alga and a fungus. Their green coloration shows up best in damp weather.

their green coloration, making them hard to see among the leaves. Parasitic wasps, too, eventually kill many of the caterpillars and only a small number of them survive to build silken cocoons and transform into moths. This is Nature's way of maintaining the balance of life in the tree. If all the leaf-eaters survived, the trees would soon be leafless.

In spring, the leaves are perfect in form, but as the summer progresses they become ragged from the feeding of insects and frayed by winds. Slowly they wear out, and by autumn are ready to be discarded. The topmost branches are the favorite hunting ground of many birds. Here, golden-crowned kinglets and gnatcatchers search for their prey, and keen-eyed hawks watch the surrounding fields for mice and rats. In the great forests of the Amazon, gorgeous *Morpho* butterflies inhabit the upper stories of the jungle trees. Lower down in the trees of our country dwell other creatures. Nuthatches and brown creepers search every crevice of the bark for insects. Lichens, too, spread their creeping growth over the trunks, tinting them with pastel shades of green. Ants crawl over every leaf and twig in their search for food. Some kinds excavate tunnels in the twigs and make their homes there. The most unusual of these are the *colobopsis* ants that make tunnels through pithy twigs. Their soldiers have plug-shaped heads, which they use like stoppers to close the entrances to their nests. The worker *colobopsis* ants gather honeydew from the leaves and when they return must be recognized by the soldier on guard before being admitted.

The trees in tropical forests teem with life of almost every sort. Here, where rains are frequent and humidity is high, there are many *epiphytes* or plants that live attached to trees. Each jungle tree is usually covered with such plants. There are orchids, ferns, airplants and mosses in great profusion. There are even some cacti that live as epiphytes high in forest trees. Here climbing vines and lianas creep up on trees, struggling to the sunshine far above the forest floor. Here live snakes, lizards, possums, rats and tree sloths. The top of a coconut palm does not look very large, but if one is cut down there is found at the

This live oak in the Everglades is festooned with streamers of Spanish moss, an air-plant that absorbs its minerals and water from the air.

Twig-girdler beetles gnaw grooves around twigs before laying their eggs in them. The twigs fall to the ground where the young beetles or grubs develop.

top of the tree where the fronds originate a great mass of tangled vegetable fiber. This is the habitat of many creatures. I found it to be the favorite nesting site of rats on the Pacific Islands. Here also live the large "flying foxes" or fruit bats.

Some insects make their homes within the living wood. *Ambrosia* beetles bore through the bark and make tunnels, which often injure the tree. Within these tunnels the beetles cultivate a special fungus or *ambrosia* upon which they feed. In time they leave the tree, carrying bits of the fungus with them. When they bore into other trees, this is used to start other fungus gardens.

Twig-girdler beetles with long antennae attack the twigs of many hardwood trees such as hickory and persimmon. As her first act in egg laying, the female cuts a neat groove around the base of a twig. This will cause the twig to die and, eventually, fall to the ground. She next deposits her eggs in small niches near the buds beyond the groove. When these eggs hatch, the larvae bore into the dying twig, feeding upon the wood. When spring comes again the adult beetles emerge and the life cycle starts over again.

147

When some kinds of trees grow old, large cavities are often formed where limbs break off. These soon become the homes of numerous animals. Here tree squirrels make nests and rear their young safe from enemies. Families of flying squirrels, too, live in these tree holes. In the dusk, they sail from tree to tree on furry "wings." Honeybees are always searching for suitable bee trees where they can establish their colonies and store honey. When they swarm, scout bees are sent out to investigate every possible site and the chosen nest is, perhaps, a tree hole. The thick walls of the tree protect the bees from cold during winter when the fields are blanketed with snow.

Sometimes these tree holes become filled with water and permanent pools are formed high above the ground. Water-loving insects soon find these hidden pools and lay their eggs. Their young live in the tree ponds. Some kinds of mosquito wigglers are found nowhere else. Most of these mosquitoes feed on other small water creatures, but some kinds have become "cannibals" and taken up the evil habit of eating other mosquito wigglers or each other. Thus, even in a tree pool high above ground, there are the hunters and the hunted. Within the tree microcosm there are smaller miscrocosms, each, as we have seen, with its special inhabitants.

A large part of any tree is found beneath the ground. The hidden roots reach out through the soil where the fine root hairs drain every available drop of moisture from the soil particles. Dissolved in this water are minerals which the tree towering above must have. Both minerals and water are pumped upward where the sucking force of the leaves takes over. Year by year the roots creep deeper into the ground seeking new supplies to feed the ever growing tree. Here in the underground darkness is yet another microcosm. It is an entirely different habitat from that in the sunlit world above ground. Surrounding the roots of many kinds of trees are cottony masses of fungus strands or *mycelia.* The fine branches of this fungus penetrate the tree

148

Tree holes are the homes of numerous animals. Within these snug retreats live squirrels, raccoons, 'possums and many insects such as honeybees.

roots, causing them to branch repeatedly and produce lichen-like structures called *mycorhizae*. In a way this fungus is a parasite, yet it actually helps the tree roots to absorb moisture and minerals. In the case of pines, this fungus has been found to benefit the tree greatly. In fact, these trees cannot live without it. In some trees, such as alder, rhododendron and sour-wood, mycorhizae penetrate the entire tree, even the seed coats. Thus, when the seed is planted the helpful fungus is present and develops along with the growing tree roots.

But this is not the end of the story. The mycorhizal fungus lives upon the roots of trees, but there are, in turn, orchids and other plants that live upon the nutrients accumulated by the fungus. In many pine forests are found coral-root orchids growing in clumps beneath the trees. The orchids contain no green chlorophyll and, so, must obtain their food from the underground fungus. I found these coral-root orchids growing in abundance in the damp pine forests found beneath the towering Teton Mountains of Wyoming. They are, of course, found in other places also, but usually are quite rare. In addition to the coral-roots, other strange plants, too, live upon the food stored up by the mycorhizae. These include the pinedrops, pinesaps and Indian pipes, all of which are pale, semi-parasitic plants of deep forests. Without the trees there would be no mycorhizae; without the mycorhizae there would be no coral-root orchids. There are three links in the chain.

Many animals, too, make their homes in the dark subterranean microcosm beneath the tree. Here the soil has been enriched by the accumulation of leaves discarded by the tree during many autumns. Through this rich humus burrow earthworms and many small insects, all feeding upon the decaying organic matter. Many caterpillars, which have spent their lives

Coral-root orchids grow on root-fungi which grow, in turn, on the roots of pine.

feeding on the foliage above ground, drop to the earth and burrow in. They form cells in the safety of the earth, transform to inactive pupae and remain all winter. With the coming of spring, some hidden instinct tells them that the time has come to emerge into the world of sunshine. The pupal cases split open and the moths push up through the surface, where they mate and lay eggs on the leaves of another spring, and another generation begins.

Strangest, perhaps, of all the denizens of the underground world are the 17-year cicadas. Like the moths, their lives begin and end in the leafy world above. The female cicadas insert their eggs into tree twigs and then fly away, perhaps to become victims of the appetites of birds. The eggs in the twigs soon hatch and the tiny, strangely formed cicadas fall to the ground and burrow in. For a year or so they are satisfied to remain near the surface, sucking nutritious sap from the tree's roots. By the second year they have moved deeper in the ground, but always near the roots which supply their food. Year after year they crawl deeper and deeper, following the root system of the tree. In summer the sap flows down from the tree and the cicadas feed; in winter the flow of sap comes to a halt and the life processes of the cicadas slow down. For seventeen years the cicada

Pinesaps also grow on the fungi of pine roots, and are without green chlorophyll.

The end of the trail for a tree and an orchid which still struggles for life on the dead wood.

nymphs alternately feed and rest. Then, during the seventeenth summer, as if alerted by a signal, they all emerge from the ground and crawl up the sides of the trees, even to the leaves. Here the adult, winged cicadas come out. This is the year of the cicadas. Within a short time, they mate and eggs are layed in the tree twigs again. They soon hatch and fall to the earth, and the long cycle starts over, timed by Nature with remarkable accuracy.

In the life of every tree there comes a time when its life processes slow down and cease to function. This may be caused

152

by a bolt of lightning, disease, insect injury or a wind storm. With the death of the tree new forms of life take up residence. Boring insects of great variety tunnel into the decaying wood, leaving their galleries filled with discarded sawdust. It would appear that grubs boring through the solid wood of a tree would be safe from harm, but they, too, have enemies. The great *Thalessa* wasp alights on the tree and knows by some unknown sense that a grub is excavating its tunnel deep inside. Slowly she drills a minute hole down into the hidden tunnel, and an egg is forced through. When it hatches, the *Thalessa's* larva feeds upon the grub.

Female engraver beetles, too, bore into dead and dying trees and make burrows beneath the bark. As they tunnel along they lay eggs. When the eggs hatch, the young beetles or grubs make little tunnels of their own, always extending at right angles to those made by the mother. As they tunnel along, the young

Engravings left on pine wood by beetles tunneling beneath the bark. The large burrows were made by egg-laying females, the smaller ones by the grubs.

beetles feed on the wood and grow larger. Their tunnels grow larger, too. When the dead bark of the tree peels away, these pretty engravings can be seen on the bare wood, etched records of the beetles' feeding and growth. Metallic wood borers, too, are attracted to dead trees, where they lay their eggs and their flat-headed larvae also mine beneath the bark.

In time the tree is invaded by termites, blind creatures of the darkness, that gnaw small galleries up from the earth where they make their nests. They are soft-bodied and defenseless, yet they are able to tunnel through the hardest wood, digesting it as they go. Night and day the termites drill through the tree, honeycombing it with passages.

As the woody tissues of the tree become filled with the tunnels of boring insects, moisture from falling rains seeps in and softens the wood even more. The spores or microscopic seeds of fungi are carried by winds to the damp wood and begin growing, sending living *mycelia* or threadlike strands through the wood. When these fungi are mature, they form millions of new spores, which are often brightly colored and which spill over the wood, staining it with rainbow hues. Strange slime molds slowly creep over the surface of the damp wood, feeding on bits of organic matter as they move along. They flow along like giant amoebae and were once considered to be some low form of animal life, though actually, they are plants related to the fungi. Some of the fungi that grow on the decaying wood are luminous and shine with a strange, greenish light in the dark. This is called "fox fire." Other fungi send their living strands down into the wood to absorb nourishment and, when the time is right, the fungal mass flows out again and forms shelflike fruiting bodies on the side of the tree. These are the bracket fungi.

High up on the dead limbs, woodpeckers hammer holes in the wood searching for boring insects. The sound of their hammering can be heard far away through the forest. Woodpeckers also excavate deep nest cavities in the dry trees, where they can

154

Woodpeckers drill holes and capture boring insects that have made their tunnels in dead trees.

lay their white eggs and rear their young in security. Flycatchers, owls, nuthatches, and chickadees take advantage of old woodpecker holes for their own nesting sites. Hawks and buzzards use the bare limbs as vantage points to survey their domains.

Thus, a tree has many lives. At first there is only the life of the tree itself, but as it grows larger it gradually becomes a teeming city inhabited by many other forms of plant and animal life that take up residence there. Each of these leads a separate existence, yet each is a part of the thriving tree community.

Index

Page numbers in italics are those on which illustrations appear.

Abscission, 55, 57
Acacia, 18, 137
Acorn, *81*
Aeschynomene, 120
Alcohol, wood, 28
Alder pollination, 67, *69*
Ailanthus, 74
Annual rings, 25
Ant, *Colobopsis*, 146
Anthocyanin, 57
Apical dominance, 36
Arkenwyke Yew, 112
Ash
    seeds, *72*
    white, 35
Aspen, 35, 51
Autumn color, 56, 57
Auxins, 36, 55, 60

Balsa, 31, *120*
Banyan, 78, *113*
Baobab, 112
Bark, 29, *31*, 32
    birch, 32
    cloth, 29
    hackberry, *34*
    pine, *32*
    white oak, *33*
Basswood, 42
Beech, 35, 42
    seeds, *83*
Beetle
    ambrosia, 147
    engraver, *153*
    twig-girdler, *147*
Birch, 24, 32, 35
Birds, 143, 154, *155*
Board foot, 28
Bois d'arc, *30*, *114*
Bottle palm, 112, 113
Breadfruit, 133, *141*
Buckeye, *40*, 43

Caffeine, 139, 140
Cambium, *22*, 29, 30
Carambola, 141
Carbon[14], 87, 88
Carob, 132
Carotene, 56
Carotenoids, 56
Catalpa
    cross-section, *114*
    pollination, 70, *71*
Cavanillesia, 31
Cedar, 25
Ceiba, 138
Cellulose, 28, 118
Charter Oak, 108
Chestnut, 42
Chicle, 132
Chinchon, Countess of, 138
Chlorophyll, 41
Chocolate, 139
Cinchona, 32, 138
Cinnamon, 137
Coco-de-mer, 77
Cocobolo, 127
Coconut palm, *128*, *131*
Coffee, 139
    bean, *140*
Coir, 130
Copra, 130, *131*
Cord, 28
Cork oak, 32
Cornel, 11
Cottonwood, 24, 35
    flower, *58*
    pollination, 68
    seeds, 77, 82, 85
Cross-pollination, 63, 67
Curare, 138
Cutin, 46
Cypress
    bald, *19*
    knee, *19*, *124*

Day-length, 61
Deciduous trees, 54, 56
Deliquescent growth, 37
Dendrochronology, 94
Dendrometer, 33
Devil's club, *34, 45*
Douglas fir, 31, 106
Douglass, A. E., 89-94
Dragon tree, 98, 112
Drip tips, 52
Druids, 11
Dueling Oak, 108, *110*
Dugout canoe, 116, *117*

Ebony, 126
Elm, *16, 17, 43*
    seeds, *72*
Epiphyte, 146
Evangeline Oak, 109
Evergreen trees, 54
Excurrent growth, 36

Fibonacci series, 38
Fig, *12*
Fir
    Douglas, 42, 106
    silver, 42
Florigen, 60
Flower
    imperfect, 63
    parts, *62,* 63
    perfect, 62
    willow, *64*
Fossil tree, *13, 86*
Founder's Tree, 102
Fructose, 132
Fungi, 154

Glucose, 132
Grant Elm, 109
Grape vine, *47*
Growth
    deliquescent, 37
    excurrent, 36
    rates, 33, 35, 36
    spirals, 38, *39*
Growth rings, *31, 89, 91*
Gum, sweet
    cross-section, *114*
    flower, *65*
    leaf, *43*

Guttation, 53

Heartwood, 23, *30, 31*
Hevea brasiliensis, 133
Holly, 12

Increment borer, 92, *93*
    cores, *95*
Insects, 145, 150-155
    beetle, *147*
    walking-stick, *144*
Ironwood
    weight of, *120*

Jaggery, 130
Juniper
    seeds of, *81*

Kapok, 138, 139, *140*
Kilmer Oak, *109*

Lanier Oak, 109
Leaves
    areas of, 42
    arrangement, 44, 54
    compound, 41
    form, 42, 52
    loss of, 55
    oak, 51
    mosaic arrangement, *45*
    scars, *56, 57*
    simple, 41
    types of, 42, *43*
    venation, *53*
Lichen, *145*
Lignin, 25, 28, 118
Lignum-vitae, 118
Locust, 18
Lotus seeds, 84

Magna Charta, 112
Magnolia, *10, 50, 107*
Mahogany, 136
Manchineel, 138
Mangrove, *20,* 78, 79
Maple
    seeds, *74*
    sugar, 132
Mark Twain, 111
Massaranduba, 132

Maté, 140
Mesquite, 18
Mimosa, 35
Mistletoe, *78, 79*, 82
Molasses, 118
Mycorhizae, 149
Myrtle, wax, 136

Nutmeg, 137

Oak, 25, *127*
    cork, 33
    live, *142*, 146
    microscopic view, *24*
    red, 35
    weight of, *120*
    white, *43*
    wood, *123*
Oak, Charter, 108
Oak, Dueling, 108, *110*
Orchid, *150, 152*
Osage orange, *30*
Osmosis, 46

Palm
    African oil, *137*
    bottle, 112, 113
    coconut, 120, 121, *128, 129, 130*
    date, 131
    nipa, *130*
    royal, *19*
    sago, 131
    wax, 136
Palmate leaves, *40*
Papaya, 141
Parliament Oak, 112
Pawpaw, *63*
Petiole, 50
Phloem, *22, 26*, 29, 30, 61
Photoperiod, 61
Photosynthesis, 41
Phyllotaxy, 54
Pine, 25, *43*
    bark, *32*
    beetles, *153*
    bristlecone, 94, 101
    cottonwood, 58, 68
    cross-section, *25, 27, 31, 99, 114, 122*
    flower, *67*

growth, 35, *37*
growth rings, *91*
jack, 35
longleaf, 133
needles, *44*
pollen, *67*
pollination, *67*, 68
ponderosa, 90, 92
seeds, 68
slash, 133
weight of, *120*
Pinedrop, 150
Pinesap, 150, *151*
Pipal, 12
Pneumatophores, *19*
Poinciana, 15
Pollen, 64-70, *66*
Pollination, 63-70
    insect, 69, 70
    wind, 64-68
Poplar, 27, 35
    cross-section of, *26*
    flower, *62*
Prickly ash, 32
Propolis, 135

Quinine, 32, 138

Redbud, 18, *43*
Redwood, *100*, 103, *105*, 106
Root pressure, 46, 48, 49
Roots
    length of, 49, 50
    magnolia, *50*
    Sequoia, 50
Rosewood, 126
Rubber, 132, 133, *134*

Samar, *75*
Sapodilla, 132
Sapwood, 24, *30, 31*
Sassafras, *40, 43*
    cross-section, *114*
Seeds
    animal dispersal, 80
    ash, *72*
    beech, *83*
    cottonwood, 77, *85*
    germination of, 82, 84, 85
    hemlock, 78
    longevity of, 82, 84, 85

maple, *74, 75*
mistletoe, 78
slippery elm, *72*
sweet gum, *83*
water dispersal, 76, 77, 78
willow, 77
wind dispersal, 74, 75, 76
Sempervirin, 122
Sequoia, 31, 50
  age, 94, 98, 99, 101
  bark, 31, 102
  Big Tree, 101, 102, 103, *104*
  coastal, *100, 105*
  General Sherman, 94, 103
  origin of name, 104
  size of, 28, 101-103
Sequoia gigantea, 103
Sequoia sempervirens, 103
Sieve tubes, 29
Silk-cotton, 138
Size, tree, 101-108
Spanish moss, 15, *146*
Spiral
  grain, 126
  growth, 38, *39*
  leaf arrangement, 54
Springwood, *25, 122, 123*
Spruce, 42
State Trees, 111
Stomates, 45, 46, 49
Stradivarius, 124
Strangler fig, 78
Strychnine, 138
Suberin, 31
Sugars, 132
Sumac, *56*
Summerwood, *25, 26, 122*, 123
Sun energy, 44
Sunspots, 89, 90, 96
Sweet gum
  flower, *65*
  seeds of, *83*

Tea, 139
Teak, 127
Thalessa wasp, 153
Tree
  buds, 59, 60
  dating of, 23, 89, *91*, 94
  definition of, 18
  fossils, *13, 86*

growth, 36-38
holes, 148, *149*
leaves of, *40*, 41-45, 50, 51
roots, 48, 49, *50*
superstitions, 13, 14, 62
wood content, 28
Tree-of-heaven, 74
Tree of Tule, 106
Tulip poplar, *22, 23*
Tung, *136*
Tupelo gum, *21*
Turpentine, 30, 132, 133, *135*

Vascular rays, *25, 26, 27*
Venation, 54

Walnut, black, *120*
Water
  lift, 46, 48
  loss, 46
  use, 49
Wawona Tree, 103
Willow, 25
  cross-section, *114*
  flower, *64*
  seeds, 77
Witch hazel, 80, 81
Wood
  balsa, *120*
  commercial uses, 28, 115-117
  compression, 124, *125*
  figured, 124
  hard, 121
  ironwood, *120*
  oak, *123*
  pine, *120*
  ring-porous, 123
  samples of, *121*
  soft, 118
  specific gravity, 118
  spiral grain, 126
  tension, 125
  tropical, 126
  walnut, *120*
  weights of, 119, *120*
Woodpecker, *155*

Xanthophyll, 56
Xylem, 24-30, *122*

Yerba maté, 140

About the Author

Entomologist Ross E. Hutchins is also an expert photographer, and this combination of interests has resulted in almost thirty years of studying, photographing and writing about insects, plants, animals and birds. Born in Montana, he grew up on a cattle ranch near Yellowstone Park. At Montana State College he majored in biological sciences and later he received his Ph.D. in zoology and entomology from Iowa State College.

Dr. Hutchins' articles and pictures of natural history subjects have appeared in encyclopedias, books and magazines, among them *National Geographic, Life* and *Natural History*, as well as such European publications as *Sie und Er, La Vie des Bêtes* and *Sciences et Avenir.* A special interest in unusual insect and plant life led to his first books in the juvenile field — INSECT BUILDERS AND CRAFTSMEN; INSECTS — HUNTERS AND TRAPPERS; STRANGE PLANTS AND THEIR WAYS; WILD WAYS. His remarkable closeup photographs are also seen in his THIS IS A LEAF and THIS IS A FLOWER, companion volumes to THIS IS A TREE.

Ross Hutchins lives in Mississippi where he is Entomologist and Executive Officer of the Mississippi State Plant Board and head of the Department of Zoology and Entomology at Mississippi State University.

65- 5250

WITHDRAWN
FROM THE RODMAN PUBLIC LIBRARY

j582   65-5250
Hutchins   2.27
This is a tree

RODMAN PUBLIC LIBRARY
ALLIANCE, OHIO